*The Heritage of
Literature Series*

SECTION A NO. 12

THE POETS' WAY

THE POETS' PATH
Complete and in Two Parts

THE POETS' WAY

STAGE I

STAGE II

STAGE III

Stages I and II in one volume

THE POETS' WAY

STAGE II

SELECTED BY

E. W. PARKER, M.C.

EDITED BY

A. R. MOON, M.A.

LONGMANS, GREEN AND CO.

LONDON · NEW YORK · TORONTO

LONGMANS, GREEN AND CO. LTD.
39 PATERNOSTER ROW, LONDON, E.C.4
CHITTARANJAN AVENUE, CALCUTTA
53 NICOL ROAD, BOMBAY
36A MOUNT ROAD, MADRAS

LONGMANS, GREEN AND CO.
114 FIFTH AVENUE, NEW YORK
221 EAST 20TH STREET, CHICAGO
88 TREMONT STREET, BOSTON

LONGMANS, GREEN AND CO.
215 VICTORIA STREET, TORONTO

First published . *April* 1936
New Impression . *January* 1937
New Impression . *August* 1937
New Impression . *December* 1937

PRINTED IN GREAT BRITAIN BY
NORTHUMBERLAND PRESS LIMITED
GATESHEAD UPON TYNE

THE HERITAGE OF LITERATURE SERIES

General Editor: E. W. PARKER, M.C.

TRAVEL AND ADVENTURE

REAL ADVENTURE
CREATURES OF THE WILDS
THE ADVENTURE OF TRAVEL
EOTHEN. By A. W. Kinglake

MORE TALES OF REAL ADVENTURE
ADVENTURES AND ENCOUNTERS
ADVENTURES ON THE HIGH SEAS
REAL ADVENTURE AGAIN

ESSAYS AND BELLES LETTRES

ENGLAND OUT OF DOORS
LIGHTER ESSAYS
STILL LIGHTER ESSAYS

ESSAYS BY MODERN WRITERS
NEW AND OLD ESSAYS
PAGES AND LEADERS

DRAMA

ONE-ACT COMEDIES

MODERN ONE-ACT PLAYS

FICTION

SHORT STORIES: OLD AND NEW
SELECTED SHORT STORIES
    By John Galsworthy, O.M.
SHORT STORIES BY MODERN
    WRITERS
THE IMAGINARY EYE-WITNESS

PILGRIM'S PROGRESS. Part I
    By John Bunyan
YOUTH AT THE HELM
ENGLISH COMIC CHARACTERS
STRANGE STORIES
A GALLANT COMPANY

MYTHS AND FOLK LORE

LEGENDS AND MYTHS OF GREECE
    AND ROME

A HERITAGE OF WONDER STORIES

HISTORY

THE ENGLAND OF QUEEN ANNE
    By George Macaulay Trevelyan, O.M.

THE IMAGINARY EYE-WITNESS

LIFE AND LETTERS

ADVENTURES AND ENCOUNTERS
ACHIEVEMENT

BIOGRAPHY OF TO-DAY

POETRY

BALLADS AND NARRATIVE POEMS
THE POETS' PATH
THE POETS' WAY. Stage I
THE POETS' WAY. Stage II
THE POETS' WAY. Stage III

AN ANTHOLOGY OF LONGER POEMS
SELECTED POEMS
    By Robert Browning
SELECTED POEMS
    By William Wordsworth

FOREWORD

LIKE the magic carpet of the story-books, poetry can transport you from your fireside corner to lands afar, to the scene of adventure and romance, or to the open road of the countryside at the spring of the year. Before poetry can give you these delights it must be read with enjoyment: take your favourite poets and let them be your companions. If it is adventure you want, poetry will give you all you desire. Without knowing how it happened, you will soon be flying on that magic carpet to join the company of those who seek high adventure.

On your way you will discover that the poets are true adventurers whose minds leap beyond the bounds of earth and send us messages that words alone cannot express.

All men are poets, but few can impart the feelings that beauty of every kind can awaken in their hearts. Listen in and attune your hearing to their messages and you will realize your own kinship with the poets.

Many poems printed here have come down to us from the past, some from times so remote that those who first sang them are unknown. This is part of the splendid heritage that is the birthright of all who speak English. When you read the modern poems in this book you will realize the continuity as well as the richness of our heritage. These poets, already deservedly famous, are with you in the quest of adventure.

E.W.P.

COMPILER'S NOTE

MANY friends have offered useful suggestions and criticisms and I should like to record my gratitude to them. I am particularly indebted to Dr. Gurrey for the generosity with which he has helped me with friendly criticism and advice.

My thanks are also due to the owners of the copyright poems and versions of older poems that are reprinted in this collection:

Mr. Norman Ault for " Sister awake! close not your eyes " from *Elizabethan Lyrics*, published by Messrs. Longmans, Green & Co. Ltd.; Mr. Hilaire Belloc and Messrs. Gerald Duckworth & Co. Ltd. for " The South Country " from *Sonnets and Verse;* the Representatives of Wilfrid Scawen Blunt and Messrs. Macmillan & Co. Ltd. for " The Old Squire " from *Poetical Works of Wilfrid Scawen Blunt;* the Representatives of Lewis Carroll and Messrs. Macmillan & Co. Ltd. for " The Walrus and the Carpenter " from *Through the Looking Glass;* the Clarendon Press, Oxford, for " The Windmill " and " London Snow " from *The Shorter Poems of Robert Bridges*, 1931, and for " Old Winter," by T. Noel, from *Smith's Book of Verse for Boys and Girls;* Messrs. R. Cobden-Sanderson Ltd. for " Autumn " from *Poems of John Clare;* Messrs. Constable & Co. Ltd. for " Juggling Jerry " from *Poems*, Volume I, by George Meredith; Mr. De la Mare for " Silver " and " Off the Ground " from *Peacock Pie*, and for " All That's Past " from *Poems 1901-1918*, published by Messrs. Constable & Co. Ltd.; Messrs. J. M. Dent & Sons Ltd. for " The Donkey," by Mr. G. K. Chesterton, and " The Thrush's Nest " from *Poems of John Clare;* Mr. W. W. Gibson and Messrs. Macmillan & Co. Ltd. for " Flannan Isle " from *Collected Poems 1905-1925;* the Executors of Thomas Hardy and Messrs. Macmillan & Co. Ltd. for " Snow in the Suburbs " and " Weathers " from *Collected Poems of Thomas Hardy;* Mr. F. W. Harvey

ix

and Messrs. Sidgwick & Jackson Ltd. for "Ducks" from *Ducks and Other Verses*; Mr. John Masefield for "Spanish Waters" and "Tewkesbury Road" from *Collected Poems*, published by Messrs. Wm. Heinemann Ltd.; Messrs. Methuen & Co. Ltd. for "Away, Haul Away" from *The Sailor's Garland*, edited by Mr. John Masefield; Sir Henry Newbolt for "Drake's Drum" from *Poems New and Old*, published by Mr. John Murray; and Mr. James Stephens and Messrs. Macmillan & Co. Ltd. for "The Snare" from *Collected Poems 1926*.

CONTENTS

xi

CONTENTS

CONTENTS

OUT OF DOORS

BIRDS AND BEASTS

xiii

CONTENTS

CONTENTS

THE PILGRIM: HIS CHARACTER

THE PILGRIM: HIS LOVE OF COUNTRY

FAREWELL

THE POETS' WAY
STAGE II

THE JOY OF READING

O for a book and a shady nook,
　Either in-doors or out;
With the green leaves whispering overhead,
　Or the street cries all about;
Where I may read all at my ease,
　Both of the new and old;
For a jolly good book whereon to look,
　Is better to me than gold.

ANONYMOUS

A ROUND OF MERRIMENT

OFF THE GROUND

Three jolly Farmers
Once bet a pound
Each dance the others would
Off the ground.
Out of their coats
They slipped right soon,
And neat and nicesome
Put each his shoon.
One—Two—Three!
And away they go,
Not too fast,
And not too slow;
Out from the elm-tree's
Noonday shadow,
Into the sun
And across the meadow.
Past the schoolroom,
With knees well bent,
Fingers a-flicking,
They dancing went.
Upsides and over,
And round and round,

They crossed click-clacking
The Parish bound;
By Tupman's meadow
They did their mile,
Tee-to-tum
On a three-barred stile.
Then straight through Whipham,
Downhill to Week,
Footing it lightsome,
But not too quick,
Up fields to Watchet,
And on through Wye,
Till seven fine churches
They'd seen skip by—
Seven fine churches,
And five old mills,
Farms in the valley,
And sheep on the hills;
Old Man's Acre
And Dead Man's Pool
All left behind,
As they danced through Wool.
And Wool gone by,
Like tops that seem
To spin in sleep
They danced in dream:
Withy—Wellover—
Wassop—Wo—
Like an old clock
Their heels did go.
A league and a league
And a league they went,

And not one weary,
And not one spent,
And lo, and behold!
Past Willow-cum-Leigh
Stretched with its waters
The great green sea.
Says Farmer Bates,
"I puffs and I blows,
What's under the water,
Why, no man knows!"
Says Farmer Giles,
"My mind comes weak,
And a good man drownded
Is far to seek."
But Farmer Turvey,
On twirling toes,
Ups with his gaiters,
And in he goes:
Down where the mermaids
Pluck and play
On their twangling harps
In a sea-green day;
Down where the mermaids,
Finned and fair,
Sleek with their combs
Their yellow hair. . . .
Bates and Giles
On the shingle sat,
Gazing at Turvey's
Floating hat.
But never a ripple
Nor bubble told

Where he was supping
Off plates of gold.
Never an echo
Rilled through the sea
Of the feasting and dancing
And minstrelsy.
They called—called—called:
Came no reply:
Nought but the ripples'
Sandy sigh.
Then glum and silent
They sat instead,
Vacantly brooding
On home and bed,
Till both together
Stood up and said:—
" Us knows not, dreams not,
Where you be,
Turvey, unless
In the deep blue sea;
But axcusing silver—
And it comes most willing—
Here's us two paying
Our forty shilling;
For it's sartin sure, Turvey,
Safe and sound,
You danced us square, Turvey,
Off the ground! "

WALTER DE LA MARE

THE WALRUS AND THE CARPENTER

The sun was shining on the sea,
Shining with all his might:
He did his very best to make
The billows smooth and bright—
And this was odd, because it was
The middle of the night.

The moon was shining sulkily,
Because she thought the sun
Had got no business to be there
After the day was done—
" It's very rude of him," she said,
" To come and spoil the fun."

The sea was wet as wet could be,
The sands were dry as dry.
You could not see a cloud, because
No cloud was in the sky:
No birds were flying overhead—
There were no birds to fly.

The Walrus and the Carpenter
Were walking close at hand;
They wept like anything to see
Such quantities of sand:
" If this were only cleared away,"
They said, " it *would* be grand! "

" If seven maids with seven mops
Swept it for half a year,
Do you suppose," the Walrus said,
" That they could get it clear? "
" I doubt it," said the Carpenter,
And shed a bitter tear.

" O Oysters, come and walk with us! "
The Walrus did beseech.
" A pleasant walk, a pleasant talk,
Along the briny beach:
We cannot do with more than four,
To give a hand to each."

The eldest Oyster looked at him,
But never a word he said:
The eldest Oyster winked his eye,
And shook his heavy head—
Meaning to say he did not choose
To leave the oyster-bed.

But four young Oysters hurried up,
All eager for the treat:
Their coats were brushed, their faces washed,
Their shoes were clean and neat—
And this was odd, because, you know,
They hadn't any feet.

Four other Oysters followed them,
And yet another four;
And thick and fast they came at last,
And more, and more, and more—
All hopping through the frothy waves,
And scrambling to the shore.

The Walrus and the Carpenter
Walked on a mile or so,
And then they rested on a rock
Conveniently low:
And all the little Oysters stood
And waited in a row.

" The time has come," the Walrus said,
" To talk of many things:
Of shoes—and ships—and sealing-wax—
Of cabbages—and kings—
And why the sea is boiling hot—
And whether pigs have wings."

" But, wait a bit," the Oysters cried,
" Before we have our chat;
For some of us are out of breath,
And all of us are fat! "
" No hurry! " said the Carpenter.
They thanked him much for that.

" A loaf of bread," the Walrus said,
" Is what we chiefly need:
Pepper and vinegar besides
Are very good indeed—
Now if you're ready, Oysters dear,
We can begin to feed."

" But not on us! " the Oysters cried,
Turning a little blue.
" After such kindness, that would be
A dismal thing to do! "
" The night is fine," the Walrus said,
" Do you admire the view?

"It was so kind of you to come:
And you are very nice! "
The Carpenter said nothing but,
"Cut us another slice:
I wish you were not quite so deaf—
I've had to ask you twice! "

"It seems a shame," the Walrus said,
"To play them such a trick,
After we've brought them out so far,
And made them trot so quick! "
The Carpenter said nothing but,
"The butter's spread too thick."

"I weep for you," the Walrus said,
"I deeply sympathize."
With sobs and tears he sorted out
Those of the largest size,
Holding his pocket-handkerchief
Before his streaming eyes.

"O Oysters," said the Carpenter,
"You've had a pleasant run!
Shall we be trotting home again? "
But answer there was none—
And this was scarcely odd, because
They'd eaten every one.

LEWIS CARROLL

THE DIVERTING HISTORY OF JOHN GILPIN

Showing how he went farther than he intended, and came safe home again

John Gilpin was a citizen
Of credit and renown,
A train-band captain eke was he
Of famous London town.

John Gilpin's spouse said to her dear—
"Though wedded we have been
These twice ten tedious years, yet we
No holiday have seen.

"To-morrow is our wedding-day,
And we will then repair
Unto the Bell at Edmonton,
All in a chaise and pair.

"My sister, and my sister's child,
Myself, and children three,
Will fill the chaise; so you must ride
On horseback after we."

He soon replied—"I do admire
Of womankind but one,
And you are she, my dearest dear,
Therefore it shall be done.

"I am a linen-draper bold,
As all the world doth know,
And my good friend the calender[1]
Will lend his horse to go."

Quoth Mrs. Gilpin—"That's well said;
And, for that wine is dear,
We will be furnished with our own,
Which is both bright and clear."

John Gilpin kissed his loving wife;
O'erjoyed was he to find
That, though on pleasure she was bent,
She had a frugal mind.

The morning came, the chaise was brought,
But yet was not allowed
To drive up to the door, lest all
Should say that she was proud.

So three doors off the chaise was stayed,
Where they did all get in;
Six precious souls, and all agog
To dash through thick and thin!

Smack went the whip, round went the wheels,
Were never folk so glad,
The stones did rattle underneath,
As if Cheapside were mad.

John Gilpin at his horse's side
Seized fast the flowing mane,
And up he got, in haste to ride,
But soon came down again;

[1] Maker of cloth.

For saddle-tree scarce reached had he,
His journey to begin,
When, turning round his head, he saw
Three customers come in.

So down he came; for loss of time,
Although it grieved him sore,
Yet loss of pence, full well he knew,
Would trouble him much more.

'Twas long before the customers
Were suited to their mind,
When Betty screaming came downstairs—
" The wine is left behind! "

" Good lack! " quoth he—" yet bring it me,
My leathern belt likewise,
In which I bear my trusty sword
When I do exercise."

Now mistress Gilpin (careful soul!)
Had two stone bottles found,
To hold the liquor that she loved,
And keep it safe and sound.

Each bottle had a curling ear,
Through which the belt he drew,
And hung a bottle on each side,
To make his balance true.

Then, over all, that he might be
Equipped from top to toe,
His long red cloak, well brushed and neat,
He manfully did throw.

Now see him mounted once again
Upon his nimble steed,
Full slowly pacing o'er the stones
With caution and good heed!

But, finding soon a smoother road
Beneath his well-shod feet,
The snorting beast began to trot,
Which galled him in his seat.

So, " Fair and softly," John he cried,
But John he cried in vain;
That trot became a gallop soon,
In spite of curb and rein.

So stooping down, as needs he must
Who cannot sit upright,
He grasped the mane with both his hands,
And eke with all his might.

His horse, who never in that sort
Had handled been before,
What thing upon his back had got
Did wonder more and more.

Away went Gilpin, neck or nought;
Away went hat and wig!—
He little dreamt, when he set out,
Of running such a rig!

The wind did blow, the cloak did fly
Like streamer long and gay,
Till, loop and button failing both,
At last it flew away.

Then might all people well discern
The bottles he had slung;
A bottle swinging at each side,
As hath been said or sung.

The dogs did bark, the children screamed,
Up flew the windows all;
And ev'ry soul cried out—" Well done! "
As loud as he could bawl.

Away went Gilpin—who but he?
His fame soon spread around—
" He carries weight! " " He rides a race! "
" 'Tis for a thousand pound! "

And still, as fast as he drew near,
'Twas wonderful to view
How in a trice the turnpike-men
Their gates wide open threw.

And now, as he went bowing down
His reeking head full low,
The bottles twain behind his back
Were shattered at a blow.

Down ran the wine into the road,
Most piteous to be seen,
Which made his horse's flanks to smoke
As they had basted been.

But still he seemed to carry weight,
With leathern girdle braced;
For all might see the bottle-necks
Still dangling at his waist.

Thus all through merry Islington
These gambols he did play,
Until he came unto the Wash[1]
Of Edmonton so gay.

And there he threw the wash[2] about
On both sides of the way,
Just like unto a trundling mop,
Or a wild goose at play.

At Edmonton his loving wife
From the balcóny spied
Her tender husband, wond'ring much
To see how he did ride.

"Stop, stop, John Gilpin!—Here's the house"—
They all at once did cry;
"The dinner waits, and we are tired."
Said Gilpin—"So am I!"

But yet his horse was not a whit
Inclined to tarry there;
For why?—his owner had a house
Full ten miles off, at Ware.

So like an arrow swift he flew,
Shot by an archer strong;
So did he fly—which brings me to
The middle of my song.

Away went Gilpin, out of breath,
And sore against his will,
Till at his friend the calender's
His horse at last stood still.

[1] A low-lying stretch of land.
[2] Pools of water lying on the marshy ground.

The calender, amazed to see
His neighbour in such trim,
Laid down his pipe, flew to the gate,
And thus accosted him:—

" What news? what news? your tidings tell;
Tell me you must and shall—
Say why bare-headed you are come,
Or why you come at all? "

Now Gilpin had a pleasant wit,
And loved a timely joke;
And thus unto the calender
In merry guise he spoke:—

" I came because your horse would come;
And, if I well forebode,
My hat and wig will soon be here—
They are upon the road."

The calender, right glad to find
His friend in merry pin,
Returned him not a single word,
But to the house went in;

Whence straight he came with hat and wig;
A wig that flowed behind,
A hat not much the worse for wear,
Each comely in its kind.

He held them up, and, in his turn,
Thus showed his ready wit—
" My head is twice as big as yours,
They therefore needs must fit.

" But let me scrape the dirt away
That hangs upon your face;
And stop and eat, for well you may
Be in a hungry case."

Said John—" It is my wedding-day,
And all the world would stare,
If wife should dine at Edmonton
And I should dine at Ware! "

So, turning to his horse, he said—
" I am in haste to dine;
'Twas for your pleasure you came here,
You shall go back for mine."

Ah, luckless speech, and bootless boast!
For which he paid full dear;
For, while he spake, a braying ass
Did sing most loud and clear;

Whereat his horse did snort, as he
Had heard a lion roar,
And galloped off with all his might,
As he had done before.

Away went Gilpin, and away
Went Gilpin's hat and wig!
He lost them sooner than at first—
For why?—they were too big!

Now, mistress Gilpin, when she saw
Her husband posting down
Into the country far away,
She pulled out half a crown;

And thus unto the youth she said
That drove them to the Bell—
" This shall be yours when you bring back
My husband safe and well."

The youth did ride, and soon did meet
John coming back amain;
Whom in a trice he tried to stop
By catching at his rein;

But, not performing what he meant,
And gladly would have done,
The frighted steed he frighted more,
And made him faster run.

Away went Gilpin, and away
Went post-boy at his heels!—
The post-boy's horse right glad to miss
The lumb'ring of the wheels.

Six gentlemen upon the road,
Thus seeing Gilpin fly,
With post-boy scamp'ring in the rear,
They raised the hue and cry:

" Stop thief! stop thief!—a highwayman! "
Not one of them was mute;
And all and each that passed that way
Did join in the pursuit.

And now the turnpike gates again
Flew open in short space;
The toll-men thinking, as before,
That Gilpin rode a race.

And so he did—and won it too!—
For he got first to town;
Nor stopped till where he had got up
He did again get down.

Now let us sing—Long live the king,
And Gilpin long live he;
And, when he next doth ride abroad,
May I be there to see!

WILLIAM COWPER

SADDLE TO RAGS

This story I'm going to sing,
  I hope it will give you content,
Concerning a silly[1] old man
  That was going to pay his rent.

As he was a-riding along,
  Along all on the highway,
A gentleman-thief overtook him,
  And thus unto him he did say:

"O well overtaken, old man,
  O well overtaken," said he:
"Thank you kindly, sir," says the old man,
  "If you be for my company."

"How far are you going this way?"
  It made the old man to smile;
"To tell you the truth, kind sir,
  I'm just a-going twa mile.

[1] Defenceless.

180

" I am but a silly old man,
　Who farms a piece of ground;
My half-year rent, kind sir,
　Just comes to forty pound.

" But my landlord's not been at hame—
　I've not seen him twelve month or more;
It makes my rent to be large,
　I've just to pay him fourscore."

" You should not have told anybody,
　For thieves they are ganging many;
If they were to light upon you
　They would rob you of every penny."

" O! never mind," says the old man,
　" Thieves I fear on no side;
My money is safe in my bags,
　In the saddle on which I ride."

As they were a-riding along,
　And riding a-down a ghyll,[1]
The thief pulled out a pistól,
　And bade the old man stand still.

The old man was crafty and false,
　As in this world are many;
He flung his old saddle o'er t' hedge,
　And said, " Fetch it, if thou'lt have any."

The thief got off his horse,
　With courage stout and bold,
To search this old man's bags,
　And gave him his horse to hold.

---

[1] A deep glen, a gully.

The old man put foot in stirrup,
    And he got on astride;
He set the thief's horse in a gallop—
    You need not bid th' old man ride!

"O stay!   O stay!" says the thief,
    "And thou half my share shalt have."
"Nay, marry, not I," quoth the old man,
    "For once I've bitten a knave!"

This thief he was not content,
    He thought there *must* be bags,
So he up with his rusty sword,
    And chopped the old saddle to rags.

The old man galloped and rode,
    Until he was almost spent,
Till he came to his landlord's house,
    And he paid him his whole year's rent.

He opened this rogue's portmantle,
    It was glorious for to behold;
There was five hundred pound in money,
    And other five hundred in gold.

ANONYMOUS

JOHN BARLEYCORN

There was three kings into the East,
    Three kings both great and high,
And they hae sworn a solemn oath,
    John Barleycorn should die.

They took a plough and ploughed him down,
  Put clods upon his head,
And they hae sworn a solemn oath,
  John Barleycorn was dead.

But the cheerful spring came kindly on,
  And showers began to fall;
John Barleycorn got up again,
  And sore surprised them all.

The sultry suns of summer came,
  And he grew thick and strong,
His head well armed wi' pointed spears,
  That no one should him wrong.

The sober autumn entered mild,
  When he grew wan and pale;
His bending joints and drooping head
  Showed he began to fail.

His colour sickened more and more,
  He faded into age;
And then his enemies began
  To show their deadly rage.

They've ta'en a weapon long and sharp,
  And cut him by the knee;
And tied him fast upon the cart,
  Like a rogue for forgerie.

They laid him down upon his back,
  And cudgelled him full sore;
They hung him up before the storm,
  And turned him o'er and o'er.

They fillèd up a darksome pit
   With water to the brim,
They heavèd in John Barleycorn,
   There let him sink or swim.

They laid him out upon the floor,
   To work him further woe,
And still, as signs of life appeared,
   They tossed him to and fro.

They wasted, o'er a scorching flame,
   The marrow of his bones;
But a miller used him worst of all,
   For he crushed him 'tween two stones.

And they hae ta'en his very heart's blood,
   And drank it round and round;
And still the more and more they drank,
   Their joy did more abound.

John Barleycorn was a hero bold,
   Of noble enterprise;
For if you do but taste his blood,
   'Twill make your courage rise.

Then let us toast John Barleycorn,
   Each man a glass in hand;
And may his great posterity
   Ne'er fail in old Scotland!

ANONYMOUS

GET UP AND BAR THE DOOR

It fell about the Martinmas time,
    And a gay time it was then,
When our goodwife got puddings to make,
    And she's boil'd them in the pan.

The wind sae cauld blew south and north,
    And blew into the floor;
Quoth our goodman to our goodwife,
    " Gae out and bar the door."

" My hand is in my hussyfskep,[1]
    Goodman, as ye may see;
An it shou'd nae be barr'd this hundred year,
    It's no be barr'd for me."

They made a paction 'tween them twa,
    They made it firm and sure,
That the first word whae'er shou'd speak
    Shou'd rise and bar the door.

Then by there came twa gentlemen,
    At twelve o'clock at night,
And they cou'd neither see house nor hall,
    Nor coal nor candle-light.

---

[1] *Hussyfskep.* A bushel basket containing grain, malt, or sugar.

" Now whether is this a rich man's house,
  Or whether it is a poor? "
But ne'er a word wad ane o' them speak,
  For barring of the door.

At first they ate the white puddings,
  And then they ate the black;
Though muckle thought the goodwife to hersel',
  Yet ne'er a word she spake.

Then said the ane unto the other,
  " Here, man, tak ye my knife;
Do ye tak off the auld man's beard,
  And I'll kiss the goodwife."—

" But there's nae water in the house,
  And what shall we do than? "—
" What ails ye at the pudding-broo,
  That boils into the pan? "

O up and started our goodman,
  An angry man was he:
" Will ye kiss my wife before my een,
  And sca'd me wi' pudding-bree? "

Then up and started our goodwife,
  Gied three skips on the floor:
" Goodman, you've spoken the foremost word!
  Get up and bar the door."

                                    ANONYMOUS

THE SONG OF THE CYCLOPS

Brave iron, brave hammer, from your sound
The art of music has her ground;
On the anvil thou keep'st time,
Thy knick-a-knock is a smith's best chime.
    Yet thwick-a-thwack, thwick, thwack-a-thwack,
      thwack,
    Make our brawny sinews crack:
    Then pit-a-pat, pat, pit-a-pat, pat,
    Till thickest bars be beaten flat.

We shoe the horses of the sun,
Harness the dragons of the moon;
Forge Cupid's quiver, bow, and arrows,
And our dame's coach that's drawn with sparrows.
    Till thwick-a-thwack, etc.

Jove's roaring cannons and his rammers
We beat out with our Lemnian hammers;
Mars his gauntlet, helm, and spear,
And Gorgon shield are all made here.
    Till thwick-a-thwack, etc.

The grate which, shut, the day outbars,
Those golden studs, which nail the stars,
The globe's case and the axle-tree,
Who can hammer these but we?
    Till thwick-a-thwack, etc.

A warming-pan to heat earth's bed,
Lying i' the frozen zone half-dead;
Hob-nails to serve the man i' the moon,
And sparrowbills to clout Pan's shoon
  Whose work but ours?
  Till thwick-a-thwack, etc.

Venus' kettles, pots, and pans
We make, or else she brawls and bans;
Tongs, shovels, and irons have their places,
Else she scratches all our faces.
  Till thwick-a-thwack, thwick, thwack-a-thwack,
    thwack,
  Make our brawny sinews crack:
  Then pit-a-pat, pat, pit-a-pat, pat,
  Till thickest bars be beaten flat.

THOMAS DEKKER

THE WEE COOPER O' FIFE

There was a wee cooper who lived in Fife,
  Nickity, nackity, noo, noo, noo.
And he has gotten a gentle wife.
  Hey Willie Wallacky, how John Dougall,
  Alane, quo' Rushety, roue, roue, roue.

She wadna bake, nor she wadna brew,
For the spoiling o' her comely hue.

She wadna card, nor she wadna spin,
For the shaming o' her gentle kin.

188

She wadna wash, nor she wadna wring,
For the spoiling o' her gouden ring.

The cooper's awa to his woo-pack,
And has laid a sheep-skin on his wife's back.

" It's I'll no' thrash ye, for your proud kin,
But I will thrash my ain sheep-skin."

" Oh, I will bake, and I will brew,
And never mair think on my comely hue.

" Oh, I will card, and I will spin,
And never mair think on my gentle kin.

" Oh, I will wash, and I will wring,
And never think mair on my gouden ring."

A' ye wha hae gotten a gentle wife
Send ye for the wee cooper o' Fife.

ANONYMOUS

THE HEIGHT OF THE RIDICULOUS

I wrote some lines upon a time
In wondrous merry mood,
And thought, as usual, men would say
They were exceeding good.

They were so queer, so very queer,
I laughed as I should die;
Albeit, in the general way,
A sober man am I.

I called my servant, and he came—
(How kind it was of him
To mind a slender man like me,
He of the mighty limb!)

He took the paper, and I watched
And saw him peep within;
At the first line he read, his face
Was all upon the grin.

He read the next,—the grin grew broad
And shot from ear to ear;
He read the third,—a chuckling noise
I now began to hear.

The fourth—he burst into a roar;
The fifth—his waistband split;
The sixth—he burst five buttons off,
And tumbled in a fit.

Ten days and nights, with sleepless eye
I watched that wretched man;
And since, I never dare to write
As funny as I can.

OLIVER WENDELL HOLMES

ADVENTURE AND ROMANCE

GREEN BROOM

There was an old man lived out in the wood,
   His trade was a-cutting of Broom, green Broom;
He had but one son without thrift, without good,
   Who lay in his bed till 'twas noon, bright noon.

The old man awoke, one morning and spoke,
   He swore he would fire the room, that room,
If his John would not rise and open his eyes,
   And away to the wood to cut Broom, green Broom.

So Johnny arose, and he slipped on his clothes,
   And away to the wood to cut Broom, green Broom,
He sharpened his knives, for once he contrives
   To cut a great bundle of Broom, green Broom.

When Johnny passed under a lady's fine house,
   Passed under a lady's fine room, fine room,
She called to her maid, " Go fetch me," she said,
   " Go fetch me the boy that sells Broom, green
     Broom."

When Johnny came in to the lady's fine house,
   And stood in the lady's fine room, fine room;

"Young Johnny," she said, "will you give up your
    trade,
  And marry a lady in bloom, full bloom?"

Johnny gave his consent, and to church they both went,
  And he wedded the lady in bloom, full bloom.
At market and fair, all folks do declare,
  There is none like the Boy that sold Broom, green
  Broom.

ANONYMOUS

THE WRAGGLE TAGGLE GIPSIES

There were three gipsies a-come to my door,
And downstairs ran this a-lady, O!
One sang high, and another sang low,
And the other sang, Bonny, bonny Biscay, O!

Then she pulled off her silk-finished gown
And put on hose of leather, O!
The ragged, ragged rags about our door—
She's gone with the wraggle taggle gipsies, O!

It was late last night, when my lord came home,
Enquiring for his a-lady, O!
The servants said, on every hand:
"She's gone with the wraggle taggle gipsies, O!"

"O saddle to me my milk-white steed.
Go and fetch me my pony, O!
That I may ride and seek my bride,
Who is gone with the wraggle taggle gipsies, O!"

O he rode high and he rode low,
He rode through woods and copses too,
Until he came to an open field,
And there he espied his a-lady, O!

" What makes you leave your house and land?
What makes you leave your money, O?
What makes you leave your new-wedded lord;
To go with the wraggle taggle gipsies, O? "

" What care I for my house and my land?
What care I for my money, O?
What care I for my new-wedded lord?
I'm off with the wraggle taggle gipsies, O! "

" Last night you slept on a goose-feather bed,
With the sheet turned down so bravely, O!
And to-night you'll sleep in a cold open field,
Along with the wraggle taggle gipsies, O! "

" What care I for a goose-feather bed,
With the sheet turned down so bravely, O?
For to-night I shall sleep in a cold open field,
Along with the wraggle taggle gipsies, O! "

ANONYMOUS

SIR PATRICK SPENS

I. *The Sailing*

The king sits in Dunfermline town
   Drinking the bluid-red wine;
" O whare will I get a skeely skipper
   To sail this new ship o' mine? "

O up and spake an eldern knight,
    Sat at the king's right knee;
" Sir Patrick Spens is the best sailor
    That ever sail'd the sea."

Our king has written a braid letter,
    And seal'd it with his hand,
And sent it to Sir Patrick Spens,
    Was walking on the strand.

" To Noroway, to Noroway,
    To Noroway o'er the faem;
The king's daughter o' Noroway,
    'Tis thou maun bring her hame."

The first word that Sir Patrick read
    So loud, loud laugh'd he;
The neist word that Sir Patrick read
    The tear blinded his e'e.

" O wha is this has done this deed
    And tauld the king o' me,
To send us out, at this time o' year,
    To sail upon the sea?

" Be it wind, be it weet, be it hail, be it sleet,
    Our ship must sail the faem;
The king's daughter o' Noroway,
    'Tis we must fetch her hame."

They hoysed their sails on Monenday morn
    Wi' a' the speed they may;
They hae landed in Noroway
    Upon a Wodensday.

II. *The Return*

" Mak ready, mak ready, my merry men a'!
  Our gude ship sails the morn."
" Now ever alack, my master dear,
  I fear a deadly storm.

" I saw the new moon late yestreen
  Wi' the auld moon in her arm;
And if we gang to sea, master,
  I fear we'll come to harm."

They hadna sail'd a league, a league,
  A league, but barely three,
When the lift[1] grew dark, and the wind blew loud
  And gurly grew the sea.

The ankers brak, and the topmast lap,
  It was sic a deadly storm:
The waves cam owre the broken ship
  Till a' her sides were torn.

" Go fetch a web o' the silken claith,
  Another o' the twine,
And wap them into our ship's side,
  And let na the sea come in."

They fetch'd a web o' the silken claith,
  Another o' the twine,
And they wapp'd them round that gude ship's
    side,
  But still the sea came in.

[1] The sky.

O laith, laith were our gude Scots lords
   To wet their cork-heel'd shoon;
But lang or a' the play was play'd
   They wat their hats aboon.

And mony was the feather bed
   That flatter'd[1] on the faem;
And mony was the gude lord's son
   That never mair cam hame.

O lang, lang may the ladies sit,
   Wi' their fans into their hand,
Before they see Sir Patrick Spens
   Come sailing to the strand!

And lang, lang may the maidens sit
   Wi' their gowd kames in their hair
A-waiting for their ain dear loves!
   For them they'll see nae mair.

Half owre, half owre to Aberdour
   'Tis fifty fathom deep;
And there lies gude Sir Patrick Spens
   Wi' the Scots lords at his feet!

ANONYMOUS

KING JOHN AND THE ABBOT OF CANTERBURY

An ancient story I'll tell you anon
Of a notable prince that was called King John;
And he ruled England with main and with might,
For he did great wrong and maintained little right.

[1] Floated.

And I'll tell you a story, a story so merry,
Concerning the Abbot of Canterbury;
How for his house-keeping, and high renown,
They rode post for him to fair London town.

An hundred men, the king did hear say,
The abbot kept in his house every day;
And fifty gold chains, without any doubt,
In velvet coats waited the abbot about.

" How now, father abbot, I hear it of thee,
Thou keepest a far better house than me,
And, for thy house-keeping and high renown,
I fear thou work'st treason against my crown."

" My liege," quo' the abbot, " I would it were known
I never spend nothing but what is my own;
And I trust your grace will do me no dere
For spending of my own true-gotten gear."

" Yes, yes, father abbot, thy fault it is high,
And now for the same thou needest must die;
For except thou canst answer me questions three,
Thy head shall be smitten from thy bodie.

" And first," quo' the king, " when I'm in this stead,
With my crown of gold so fair on my head,
Among all my liegemen so noble of birth,
Thou must tell me to one penny what I am worth.

" Secondly, tell me, without any doubt,
How soon I may ride the whole world about.
And at the third question thou must not shrink,
But tell me here truly what I do think."

" O, these are hard questions for my shallow wit,
Nor I cannot answer your grace as yet:
But if you will give me but three weeks' space,
I'll do my endeavour to answer your grace."

" Now three weeks' space to thee will I give,
And that is the longest thou hast to live;
For if thou dost not answer my questions three,
Thy lands and thy livings are forfeit to me."

Away rode the abbot all sad at that word,
And he rode to Cambridge and Oxenford;
But never a doctor there was so wise
That could with his learning an answer devise.

Then home rode the abbot of comfort so cold,
And he met his shepherd a-going to fold:
" How now, my lord abbot, you are welcome home;
What news do you bring us from good King John? "

" Sad news, sad news, shepherd, I must give:
That I have but three more days to live;
For if I do not answer him questions three,
My head will be smitten from my bodie.

" The first is to tell him there in that stead,
With his crown of gold so fair on his head,
Among all his liegemen so noble of birth,
To within one penny of what he is worth.

" The second to tell him, without any doubt,
How soon he may ride this whole world about:
And at the third question I must not shrink,
To tell him there truly what he does think."

" Now cheer up, sir abbot!   Did thou never hear yet,
That a fool he may learn a wise man wit?
Lend me your serving-men, horse and apparel,
And I'll ride to London to answer your quarrel.

" Nay, frown not, if it hath been told unto me,
I am like your lordship as ever may be:
And if you will but lend me your gown,
There is none shall know us at fair London town."

" Now horses and serving-men thou shalt have,
With sumptuous array most gallant and brave,
With crozier and mitre, and rochet and cope,
Fit to appear 'fore our father the pope."

" Now welcome, sir abbot," the king he did say,
" 'Tis well thou'rt come back to keep thy day;
For and if thou canst answer my questions three,
Thy life and thy living both savèd shall be.

" And first when thou seest me here in this stead,
With my crown of gold so fair on my head,
Among all my liegemen so noble of birth,
Tell me to one penny what I am worth."

" For thirty pence our Saviour was sold
Among the false Jews, as I have been told;
And twenty-nine is the worth of thee,
For I think thou'rt one penny worser than He."

The king he laughed and swore by St. Bittel:
" I did not think I had been worth so little!
—Now secondly tell me, without any doubt,
How soon I may ride this whole world about."

" You must rise with the sun, and ride with the same,
Until the next morning he riseth again;
And then your grace need not make any doubt,
But in twenty-four hours you'll ride it about."

The king he laughed and swore by St. John:
" I did not think I could do it so soon!
—Now from the third question thou must not shrink,
But tell me here truly what I do think."

" Yea, that shall I do, and make your grace merry:
You think I'm the abbot of Canterbury;
But I'm his poor shepherd, as plain you may see,
That am come to beg pardon for him and for me."

The king he laughed, and swore by the mass,
" I'll make thee lord abbot this day in his place! "
" Now nay, my liege, be not in such speed,
For alack! I can neither write nor read."

" Four nobles[1] a week then I will give thee,
For this merry jest thou hast shown unto me;
And tell the good abbot, when thou comest home,
Thou hast brought him a pardon from good King
    John."

ANONYMOUS

ROBIN HOOD AND ALAN A DALE

Come listen to me, you gallants so free,
   All you that love mirth for to hear,
And I will you tell of a bold outláw,
   That lived in Nottinghamshire.

[1] An anachronism. A noble was a gold coin worth 6s. 8d. (or
10s), first minted by Edward III.

As Robin Hood in the forest stood,
　　All under the green-wood tree,
There was he ware of a brave young man,
　　As fine as fine might be.

The youngster was clothed in scarlet red,
　　In scarlet fine and gay,
And he did frisk it over the plain,
　　And chanted a roundelay.

As Robin Hood next morning stood,
　　Amongst the leaves so gay,
There did he espy the same young man
　　Come drooping along the way.

The scarlet he wore the day before,
　　It was clean cast away;
And every step he fetched a sigh,
　　" Alack and a well a day! "

Then steppèd forth brave Little John,
　　And Much the miller's son,
Which made the young man bend his bow,
　　When as he saw them come.

" Stand off, stand off! " the young man said,
　　" What is your will with me? "—
" You must come before our master straight,
　　Under yon green-wood tree."

And when he came bold Robin before,
　　Robin asked him courteously,
" O hast thou any money to spare,
　　For my merry men and me? "

"I have no money," the young man said,
  "But five shillings and a ring;
And that I have kept this seven long years,
  To have it at my wedding.

"Yesterday I should have married a maid,
  But she is now from me ta'en,
And chosen to be an old knight's delight,
  Whereby my poor heart is slain."

"What is thy name?" then said Robin Hood,
  "Come tell me, without any fail."—
"By the faith of my body," then said the
    young man,
  "My name it is Alan a Dale."

"What wilt thou give me," said Robin Hood,
  "In ready gold or fee,
To help thee to thy true-love again,
  And deliver her unto thee?"

"I have no money," then quoth the young
    man,
  "No ready gold nor fee,
But I will swear upon a book
  Thy true servant for to be."—

"But how many miles to thy true-love?
  Come tell me without any guile."—
"By the faith of my body," then said the
    young man,
  "It is but five little mile."

Then Robin he hasted over the plain,
    He did neither stint nor lin,[1]
Until he came unto the church
    Where Alan should keep his wedding.

" What dost thou do here? " the Bishop he
      said,
    " I prithee now tell to me."
" I am a bold harper," quoth Robin Hood,
    " And the best in the north country."

" O welcome, O welcome! " the Bishop he said,
    " That music best pleaseth me."—
" You shall have no music," quoth Robin Hood,
    " Till the bride and the bridegroom I see."

With that came in a wealthy knight,
    Which was both grave and old,
And after him a finikin[2] lass,
    Did shine like glistering gold.

" This is no fit match," quoth bold Robin
      Hood,
    " That you do seem to make here;
For since we are come unto the church,
    The bride she shall choose her own dear."

Then Robin Hood put his horn to his mouth,
    And blew blasts two or three;
When four and twenty bowmen bold
    Come leaping over the lee.

And when they came into the churchyard,
    Marching all on a row,

    [1] Tarry, delay.   [2] Dainty.

The first man was Alan a Dale,
  To give bold Robin his bow.

"This is thy true-love," Robin he said,
  "Young Alan, as I hear say;
And you shall be married at this same time,
  Before we depart away."

"That shall not be," the Bishop he said,
  "For thy word it shall not stand;
They shall be three times asked in the church,
  As the law is of our land."

Robin Hood pull'd off the Bishop's coat,
  And put it upon Little John;
"By the faith of my body," then Robin said,
  "The cloth doth make thee a man."

When Little John went into the choir,
  The people began for to laugh;
He asked them seven times in the church,
  Lest three should not be enough.

"Who gives me this maid?" then said Little
    John.
  Quoth Robin, "That do I!
And he that doth take her from Alan a Dale
  Full dearly he shall her buy."

And thus having ended this merry wedding,
  The bride looked as fresh as a queen,
And so they returned to the merry green-
    wood,
  Amongst the leaves so green.

ANONYMOUS

BRUCE'S ADDRESS BEFORE BANNOCKBURN

Scots, wha hae wi' Wallace bled,
Scots, wham Bruce has aften led;
Welcome to your gory bed,
   Or to victorie!

Now's the day, and now's the hour;
See the front o' battle lour;
See approach proud Edward's power—
   Chains and slaverie!

Wha will be a traitor knave?
Wha can fill a coward's grave?
Wha sae base as be a slave?
   Let him turn and flee!

Wha for Scotland's King and law
Freedom's sword will strongly draw,
Freeman stand, or freeman fa',
   Let him follow me!

By oppression's woes and pains!
By your sons in servile chains!
We will drain our dearest veins,
   But they shall be free!

Lay the proud usurpers low!
Tyrants fall in every foe!
Liberty's in every blow!
   Let us do, or die!

ROBERT BURNS

AGINCOURT

Fair stood the wind for France,
When we our sails advance,
Nor now to prove our chance
   Longer will tarry;
But putting to the main,
At Kaux, the mouth of Seine,
With all his martial train,
   Landed King Harry.

And taking many a fort,
Furnish'd in warlike sort,
Marcheth towards Agincourt
   In happy hour;
Skirmishing day by day
With those that stopp'd his way,
Where the French general lay
   With all his power.

Which in his height of pride,
King Henry to deride,
His ransom to provide
   To the king sending;
Which he neglects the while,
As from a nation vile,
Yet with an angry smile
   Their fall portending.

And turning to his men,
Quoth our brave Henry then,
" Though they to one be ten,
   Be not amazèd:
206

Yet have we well begun,
Battles so bravely won
Have ever to the sun
　　By fame been raisèd.

" And for myself," quoth he,
" This my full rest shall be,
England ne'er mourn for me,
　　Nor more esteem me:
Victor I will remain,
Or on this earth lie slain,
Never shall she sustain
　　Loss to redeem me.

" Poitiers and Cressy tell,
When most their pride did swell,
Under our swords they fell:
　　No less our skill is
Than when our grandsire great,
Claiming the regal seat,
By many a warlike feat
　　Lopp'd the French lilies."

The Duke of York so dread,
The eager vaward[1] led;
With the main Henry sped,
　　Amongst his henchmen.
Exeter had the rear,
A braver man not there;
Heavens! how hot they were
　　On the false Frenchmen!

[1] Vanguard.

They now to fight are gone;
Armour on armour shone,
Drum now to drum did groan;
　To hear was wonder;
That with the cries they make
The very earth did shake;
Trumpet to trumpet spake,
　Thunder to thunder.

Well it thine age became,
O noble Erpingham,
Which didst the signal aim
　To our hid forces;
When from a meadow by,
Like a storm suddenly,
The English archery
　Stuck the French horses.

With Spanish yew so strong,
Arrows a cloth-yard long,
That like to serpents stung,
　Piercing the weather;
None from his fellow starts,
But playing manly parts,
And like true English hearts,
　Stuck close together.

When down their bows they threw,
And forth their bilboes drew,
And on the French they flew;
　Not one was tardy;

Arms were from shoulders sent,
Scalps to the teeth were rent,
Down the French peasants went,
　　Our men were hardy.

This while our noble king,
His broad sword brandishing,
Down the French host did ding,[1]
　　As to o'erwhelm it;
And many a deep-wound lent,
His arms with blood besprent,
And many a cruel dent
　　Bruisèd his helmet.

Gloucester, that duke so good,
Next of the royal blood,
For famous England stood,
　　With his brave brother,
Clarence, in steel so bright,
Though but a maiden knight,
Yet in that furious fight
　　Scarce such another.

Warwick in blood did wade,
Oxford the foe invade,
And cruel slaughter made,
　　Still as they ran up;
Suffolk his axe did ply,
Beaumont and Willoughby
Bare them right doughtily,
　　Ferrers and Fanhope.

[1] Beat down with resounding blows.

Upon Saint Crispin's day
Fought was this noble fray,
Which fame did not delay
   To England to carry:
O when shall Englishmen
With such acts fill a pen,
Or England breed again
   Such a King Harry!

MICHAEL DRAYTON

A LYKE-WAKE DIRGE

This ae nighte, this ae nighte
   —*Every nighte and alle,*
Fire and fleet[1] and candle-lighte,
   And Christe receive thy saule.

When thou from hence away art past,
   —*Every nighte and alle,*
To Whinny-muir[2] thou com'st at last;
   And Christe receive thy saule.

If ever thou gavest hosen and shoon,
   —*Every nighte and alle,*
Sit thee down and put them on;
   And Christe receive thy saule.

If hosen and shoon thou ne'er gav'st nane,
   —*Every nighte and alle,*
The whinnes sall prick thee to the bare bane;
   And Christe receive thy saule.

[1] Other versions have *sleet* or *salt*. In John Aubrey's seventeenth century MS. he gives *fleet* and explains it as meaning water. It means the flowing away of water, suggesting the passing away of life.
[2] A moor covered with furze bushes.

From Whinny-muir when thou may'st pass,
   —*Every nighte and alle,*
To Brig o' Dread thou com'st at last;
   And Christe receive thy saule.

From Brig o' Dread when thou may'st pass,
   —*Every nighte and alle,*
To Purgatory fire thou com'st at last;
   And Christe receive thy saule.

If ever thou gavest meat or drink,
   —*Every nighte and alle,*
The fire sall never make thee shrink;
   And Christe receive thy saule.

If meat and drink thou ne'er gav'st nane,
   —*Every nighte and alle,*
The fire will burn thee to the bare bane;
   And Christe receive thy saule.

This ae nighte, this ae nighte,
   —*Every nighte and alle,*
Fire and fleet and candle-lighte,
   And Christe receive thy saule.

ANONYMOUS

THOMAS RYMER

True Thomas lay o'er yond grassy bank,
   And he beheld a ladie gay,
A ladie that was brisk and bold,
   Come riding o'er the fernie brae.

Her skirt was of the grass-green silk,
    Her mantel of the velvet fine,
At ilka tett[1] of her horse's mane
    Hung fifty silver bells and nine.

True Thomas he took off his hat,
    And bowed him low down till his knee:
" All hail, thou mighty Queen of Heaven!
    For your peer on earth I never did see."

" O no, O no, True Thomas," she says,
    " That name does not belong to me;
I am but the queen of fair Elfland,
    And I'm come here for to visit thee.

" But ye maun go wi' me now, Thomas,
    True Thomas, ye maun go wi' me,
For ye maun serve me seven years,
    Thro' weel or wae, as may chance to be.

" Then harp and carp,[2] Thomas," she said,
    " Then harp and carp alang wi' me;
But it will be seven years and a day
    Till ye win back to yere ain countrie."

She turned about her milk-white steed,
    And took True Thomas up behind,
And aye whene'er her bridle rang,
    The steed flew swifter than the wind.

For forty days and forty nights
    He wade thro' red blude to the knee,
And he saw neither sun nor moon,
    But heard the roaring of the sea.

[1] A lock of hair.
[2] Converse   Chaucer applies this word to the merry talk of the Wife of Bath.

O they rade on, and further on,
  Until they came to a garden green:
" Light down, light down, ye ladie free,
  Some of that fruit let me pull to thee."

" O no, O no, True Thomas," she says,
  " That fruit maun not be touched by thee,
For a' the plagues that are in hell
  Light on the fruit of this countrie.

" But I have a loaf here in my lap,
  Likewise a bottle of claret wine,
And now ere we go farther on,
  We'll rest a while, and ye may dine."

When he had eaten and drunk his fill:—
  " Lay down your head upon my knee,"
The lady sayd, " ere we climb yon hill
  And I will show you fairlies¹ three.

" O see not ye yon narrow road,
  So thick beset wi' thorns and briers?
That is the path of righteousness,
  Tho' after it but few inquires.

" And see not ye that braid, braid road,
  That lies across yon lillie leven?²
That is the path of wickedness,
  Tho' some call it the road to heaven.

" And see not ye that bonny road,
  Which winds about the fernie brae?
That is the road to fair Elfland,
  Where you and I this night maun gae.

¹ Marvels.
² ? Lily-covered plain. *Leven* does not appear to be connected with *lawn*.

213

" But Thomas, ye maun hold your tongue,
    Whatever you may hear or see,
For gin ae word you should chance to speak,
    You will ne'er get back to your ain
        countrie."

He has gotten a coat of the even cloth,
    And a pair of shoes of velvet green,
And till seven years were past and gone
    True Thomas on earth was never seen.

ANONYMOUS

THE TWA CORBIES

As I was walking all alane,
I heard twa corbies making a mane;
The tane unto the t'other gan say,
" Where sall we gang and dine to-day? "

" In behint yon auld fail dyke,[1]
I wot there lies a new-slain knight;
And naebody kens that he lies there,
But his hawk, his hound, and his lady fair.

" His hound is to the hunting gane,
His hawk to fetch the wild-fowl hame,
His lady's ta'en another mate,
So we may mak' our dinner sweet.

" Ye sall sit on his white hause-bane,[2]
And I'll pike out his bonnie blue een.

[1] Turfed bank.   [2] Collar-bone.

Wi' ae lock o' his gowden hair
We'll theek[1] our nest when it grows bare.

" Mony a one for him maks mane,
But nane sall ken where he is gane:
O'er his white banes, when they are bare,
The wind sall blaw for evermair."

ANONYMOUS

[1] Thatch, *i.e.* repair.

THE FLOWERS OF THE FOREST

I've heard them lilting at our ewe-milking,
Lasses a'lilting before the dawn of day;
But now they are moaning on ilka green loaning[1]—
The Flowers of the Forest are a' wede away.

At bughts,[2] in the morning, nae blythe lads are scorning,
The lasses are lonely, and dowie, and wae;
Nae daffin',[3] nae gabbin', but sighing and sabbing.
Ilk ane lifts her leglin[4] and hies her away.

In har'st, at the shearing, nae youths now are jeering,
The bandsters[5] are lyart,[6] and runkled,[7] and gray;
At fair or at preaching, nae wooing, nae fleeching[8]—
The Flowers of the Forest are a' wede away.

At e'en, in the gloaming, nae younkers are roaming
'Bout stacks wi' the lasses at bogle to play;
But ilk ane sits drearie, lamenting her dearie—
The Flowers of the Forest are weded away.

[1] Milking-ground.　　[2] Cattle pens.　　[3] Jesting.　　[4] Milk-pail.
[5] Binders of sheaves.　　[6] Grizzled.　　[7] Wrinkled.　　[8] Wheedling

Dool[1] and wae for the order sent our lads to the Border!
The English, for ance, by guile wan the day;
The Flowers of the Forest, that fought aye the foremost,
The prime of our land, are cauld in the clay.

We'll hear nae mair lilting at our ewe-milking;
Women and bairns are heartless and wae;
Sighing and moaning on ilka green loaning—
The Flowers of the Forest are a' wede away.

JEAN ELLIOT

BINNORIE

There were twa sisters sat in a bour;
    Binnorie, O Binnorie!
There cam a knight to be their wooer,
    By the bonnie mill-dams o' Binnorie.

He courted the eldest with glove and ring,
But he lo'ed the youngest abune a'thing.

The eldest she was vexèd sair,
And sair envied her sister fair.

Upon a morning fair and clear,
She cried upon her sister dear:

" O sister, sister, tak my hand,
And we'll see our father's ships to land."

She's ta'en her by the lily hand,
And led her down to the river-strand.

The youngest stood upon a stane,
The eldest cam and pushed her in.

---

[1] Grief; dole.

" O sister, sister, reach your hand!
And ye shall be heir o' half my land:

" O sister, reach me but your glove!
And sweet William shall be your love."

" Foul fa' the hand that I should take;
It twin'd me o' my warldis make.[1]

" Your cherry cheeks and your yellow hair
Gar'd me gang maiden evermair."

Sometimes she sank, sometimes she swam,
Until she cam to the miller's dam.

Out then cam the miller's son,
And saw the fair maid soummin' in.

" O father, father, draw your dam!
There's either a mermaid or a milk-white swan."

The miller hasted and drew his dam,
And there he found a drowned woman.

You couldna see her middle sma',
Her gowden girdle was sae braw.

You couldna see her lily feet,
Her gowden fringes were sae deep.

You couldna see her yellow hair
For the strings o' pearls was twisted there.

You couldna see her fingers sma'
Wi' diamond rings they were cover'd a'.

And by there cam a harper fine,
That harpit to the king at dine.

[1] Severed me from the one chosen to be my mate in this world.

And when he looked that lady on,
He sighed and made a heavy moan.

He's made a harp of her breast-bane,
Whose sound would melt a heart of stane.

He's ta'en three locks o' her yellow hair,
And wi' them strung his harp sae rare.

He went into her father's hall,
And there was the court assembled all.

He laid his harp upon a stane,
And straight it began to play alane.

"O yonder sits my father, the King,
And yonder sits my mother, the Queen;

"And yonder stands my brother Hugh,
And by him my William, sweet and true."

But the last tune that the harp played then—
    Binnorie, O Binnorie!—
Was, "Woe to my sister, false Helén!"—
    By the bonnie mill-dams o' Binnorie.

ANONYMOUS

PIBROCH[1] OF DONUIL DHU

Pibroch of Donuil Dhu,
    Pibroch of Donuil,
Wake thy wild voice anew,
    Summon Clan Conuil.

[1] Martial notes from the bagpipes.

Come away, come away,
   Hark to the summons!
Come in your war array,
   Gentles and commons!

Come from deep glen, and
   From mountain so rocky;
The war-pipe and pennon
   Are at Inverlochy.
Come every hill-plaid, and
   True heart that wears one;
Come every steel blade, and
   Strong hand that bears one!

Leave untended the herd,
   The flock without shelter;
Leave the corpse uninterred,
   The bride at the altar.
Leave the deer, leave the steer,
   Leave nets and barges;
Come with your fighting-gear,
   Broadswords and targes.

Come as the winds come, when
   Forests are rended:
Come as the waves come, when
   Navies are stranded.
Faster come, faster come,
   Faster and faster;
Chief, vassal, page, and groom,
   Tenant and master.

Fast they come, fast they come;
    See how they gather!
Wide waves the eagle plume,
    Blended with heather.
Cast your plaids, draw your blades,
    Forward, each man, set!
Pibroch of Donuil Dhu,
    Knell for the onset!

SIR WALTER SCOTT

COCK UP YOUR BEAVER

When first my brave Johnnie lad
    Came to this town,
He had a blue bonnet
    That wanted the crown;
But now he has gotten
    A hat and a feather,—
Hey, brave Johnnie lad,
    Cock up your beaver!

Cock up your beaver,
    And cock it fu' sprush,[1]
We'll over the border
    And gie them a brush:
There's somebody there
    We'll teach better behaviour—
Hey, brave Johnnie lad,
    Cock up your beaver!

ROBERT BURNS

[1] Spruce, brisk.

THE WIFE OF USHER'S WELL

There lived a wife at Usher's Well,
    And a wealthy wife was she;
She had three stout and stalwart sons,
    And sent them o'er the sea.

They hadna been a week from her,
    A week but barely ane,
When word came to the carline[1] wife
    That her three sons were gane.

They hadna been a week from her,
    A week but barely three,
When word came to the carline wife
    That her sons she'd never see.

" I wish the wind may never cease,
    Nor fishes[2] in the flood,
Till my three sons come hame to me
    In earthly flesh and blood! "

It fell about the Martinmas,
    When nights are lang and mirk,
The carline wife's three sons came hame,
    And their hats were o' the birk.[3]

It neither grew in syke[4] nor ditch,
    Nor yet in ony sheugh,[5]
But at the gates o' Paradise
    That birk grew fair eneugh.

[1] Old woman.
[2] Other versions have *fashes* (troubles) or *freshes*.
[3] Birch.
[4] Marshy runlet.
[5] Possibly a variant of *shaw*, a wood, but more likely another word meaning a deep ditch.

" Blow up the fire, my maidens!
   Bring water from the well!
For all my house shall feast this night,
   Since my three sons are well."

And she has made to them a bed,
   She's made it large and wide;
And she's ta'en her mantle her about,
   Sat down at the bedside.

Then up and crew the red, red cock,
   And up and crew the grey;
The eldest to the youngest said,
   " 'Tis time we were away."

The cock he hadna craw'd but ance,
   And clapp'd his wings at a',
When the youngest to the eldest said,
   " Brother, we must awa'."

" The cock doth craw, the day doth daw,
   The channerin'[1] worm doth chide;
Gin we be miss'd out o' our place,
   A sair pain we must bide."—

" Lie still, lie still but a little wee while,
   Lie still but if we may;
Gin my mother should miss us when she wakes,
   She'll go mad ere it be day."—

" Fare ye weel, my mother dear!
   Fareweel to barn and byre![2]
And fare ye weel, the bonny lass
   That kindles my mother's fire! "

ANONYMOUS

[1] Fretting.   [2] Cattle shed.

TOM O' BEDLAM

The moon's my constant mistress,
And the lonely[1] owl my marrow;
    The flaming drake,
    And the night-crow, make
Me music to my sorrow.

I know more than Apollo;
For oft, when he lies sleeping,
    I behold the stars
    At mortal wars,
And the rounded welkin weeping.

The moon embraces her shepherd,
And the Queen of Love her warrior;
    While the first does horn
    The stars of the morn,
And the next the heavenly farrier.

With a host of furious fancies,
Whereof I am commander:
    With a burning spear,
    And a horse of air,
To the wilderness I wander.

With a Knight of ghosts and shadows,
I summoned am to Tourney:
    Ten leagues beyond
    The wide world's end;
Methinks it is no journey.

ANONYMOUS

[1] Other versions have *lowly* or *lovely*.

HOW THEY BROUGHT THE GOOD NEWS FROM GHENT TO AIX

I

I sprang to the stirrup, and Joris, and he;
I galloped, Dirck galloped, we galloped all three;
" Good speed! " cried the watch, as the gate-bolts
    undrew;
" Speed! " echoed the wall to us galloping through;
Behind shut the postern, the lights sank to rest,
And into the midnight we galloped abreast.

II

Not a word to each other; we kept the great pace
Neck by neck, stride by stride, never changing our place;
I turned in my saddle and made its girths tight,
Then shortened each stirrup, and set the pique right,
Rebuckled the cheek-strap, chained slacker the bit,
Nor galloped less steadily Roland a whit.

III

'Twas moonset at starting; but while we drew near
Lokeren, the cocks crew and twilight dawned clear;
At Boom, a great yellow star came out to see;
At Düffeld, 'twas morning as plain as could be;
And from Mecheln church-steeple we heard the half-
    chime,
So Joris broke silence with, " Yet there is time! "

IV

At Aerschot, up leaped of a sudden the sun,
And against him the cattle stood black every one,
To stare thro' the mist at us galloping past,
And I saw my stout galloper Roland at last,
With resolute shoulders, each butting away
The haze, as some bluff river headland its spray.

V

And his low head and crest, just one sharp ear bent
    back
For my voice, and the other pricked out on his track;
And one eye's black intelligence,—ever that glance
O'er its white edge at me, his own master, askance!
And the thick heavy spume-flakes where aye and anon
His fierce lips shook upwards in galloping on.

VI

By Hasselt, Dirck groaned; and, cried Joris, " Stay
    spur!
Your Roos galloped bravely, the fault's not in her,
We'll remember at Aix "—for one heard the quick
    wheeze
Of her chest, saw the stretched neck and staggering
    knees,
And sunk tail, and horrible heave of the flank,
As down on her haunches she shuddered and sank.

VII

So we were left galloping, Joris and I,
Past Looz and pass Tongres, no cloud in the sky;

The broad sun above laughed a pitiless laugh,
'Neath our feet broke the brittle bright stubble like
    chaff;
Till over by Dalhem a dome-spire sprang white,
And " Gallop," gasped Joris, " for Aix is in sight! "

VIII

" How they'll greet us! "—and all in a moment his roan
Rolled neck and croup over, lay dead as a stone;
And there was my Roland to bear the whole weight
Of the news which alone could save Aix from her fate,
With his nostrils like pits full of blood to the brim,
And with circles of red for his eye-sockets' rim.

IX

Then I cast loose my buffcoat, each holster let fall,
Shook off both my jack-boots, let go belt and all,
Stood up in the stirrup, leaned, patted his ear,
Called my Roland his pet-name, my horse without peer;
Clapped my hands, laughed and sang, any noise, bad
    or good,
Till at length into Aix Roland galloped and stood.

X

And all I remember is—friends flocking round
As I sat with his head 'twixt my knees on the ground;
And no voice but was praising this Roland of mine,
As I poured down his throat our last measure of wine,
Which (the burgesses voted by common consent)
Was no more than his due who brought good news
    from Ghent.

ROBERT BROWNING

CAVALIER SONG

Kentish Sir Byng stood for his King,
Bidding the crop-headed Parliament swing:
And, pressing a troop unable to stoop
And see the rogues flourish and honest folk droop,
Marched them along, fifty-score strong,
Great-hearted gentlemen, singing this song.

God for King Charles!   Pym and such carles
To the Devil that prompts 'em their treasonous parles!
Cavaliers, up!   Lips from the cup,
Hands from the pasty, nor bite take nor sup
Till you're—
   CHORUS.—*Marching along, fifty-score strong,*
       Great-hearted gentlemen, singing this song.

Hampden to hell, and his obsequies' knell
Serve Hazelrig, Fiennes, and young Harry as well!
England, good cheer!   Rupert is near!
Kentish and loyalists, keep we not here
   CHORUS.—*Marching along, fifty-score strong,*
       Great-hearted gentlemen, singing this song?

Then, God for King Charles!   Pym and his snarls
To the Devil that pricks on such pestilent carles!
Hold by the right, you double your might;
So, onward to Nottingham, fresh for the fight,
   CHORUS.—*March we along, fifty-score strong,*
       Great-hearted gentlemen, singing this song!
              ROBERT BROWNING

THE SONG OF THE WESTERN MEN
1688

A good sword and a trusty hand!
  A merry heart and true!
King James's men shall understand
  What Cornish lads can do.

And have they fixed the where and when?
  And shall Trelawny die?
Here's twenty thousand Cornish men
  Will know the reason why!

Out spake their captain brave and bold,
  A merry wight was he:
" If London Tower were Michael's hold,
  We'll set Trelawny free!

" We'll cross the Tamar, land to land,
  The Severn is no stay,—
With ' one and all,'[1] and hand in hand,
  And who shall bid us nay?

" And when we come to London Wall,
  A pleasant sight to view,
Come forth! Come forth, ye cowards all,
  Here's men as good as you!

" Trelawny he's in keep and hold,
  Trelawny he may die;—
But here's twenty thousand Cornish bold
  Will know the reason why! "

ROBERT STEPHEN HAWKER

[1] The Cornish motto.

228

ON THE HIGH SEAS

THE SALCOMBE SEAMAN'S FLAUNT TO THE PROUD PIRATE

A lofty ship from Salcombe came,
  Blow high, blow low, and so sailed we;
She had golden trucks that shone like flame,
  On the bonny coasts of Barbary.

" Masthead, masthead," the captain's hail,
  Blow high, blow low, and so sailed we;
" Look out and round; d'ye see a sail? "
  On the bonny coasts of Barbary.

" There's a ship that looms like Beachy Head,"
  Blow high, blow low, and so sailed we;
" Her banner aloft it blows out red,"
  On the bonny coasts of Barbary.

" Oh, ship ahoy, and where do you steer? "
  Blow high, blow low, and so sailed we;
" Are you man-of-war, or privateer? "
  On the bonny coasts of Barbary.

" I am neither one of the two," said she,
  Blow high, blow low, and so sailed we;
" I'm a pirate looking for my fee,"
  On the bonny coasts of Barbary.

"I'm a jolly pirate, out for gold:"
   Blow high, blow low, and so sailed we;
"I will rummage through your after hold,"
   On the bonny coasts of Barbary.

The grumbling guns they flashed and roared,
   Blow high, blow low, and so sailed we;
Till the pirate's masts went overboard,
   On the bonny coasts of Barbary.

They fired shot till the pirate's deck,
   Blow high, blow low, and so sailed we;
Was blood and spars and broken wreck,
   On the bonny coasts of Barbary.

"O do not haul the red flag down,"
   Blow high, blow low, and so sailed we;
"O keep all fast until we drown,"
   On the bonny coasts of Barbary.

They called for cans of wine, and drank,
   Blow high, blow low, and so sailed we;
They sang their songs until she sank,
   On the bonny coasts of Barbary.

Now let us brew good cans of flip,[1]
   Blow high, blow low, and so sailed we;
And drink a bowl to the Salcombe ship,
   On the bonny coasts of Barbary.

And drink a bowl to the land of fame,
   Blow high, blow low, and so sailed we;
Who put the pirate ship to shame,
   On the bonny coasts of Barbary.

ANONYMOUS

[1] A slightly warmed mixture of beer and spirit.

DRAKE'S DRUM

Drake he's in his hammock an' a thousand mile away,
   (Capten, art tha sleepin' there below?),
Slung atween the round shot in Nombre Dios Bay,
   An' dreamin' arl the time o' Plymouth Hoe.
Yarnder lumes the Island, yarnder lie the ships,
   Wi' sailor-lads a-dancin' heel-an'-toe,
An' the shore-lights flashin', and the night-tide dashin',
   He sees et arl so plainly as he saw et long ago.

Drake he was a Devon man, an' rüled the Devon seas,
   (Capten, art tha sleepin' there below?),
Rovin' tho' his death fell, he went wi' heart at ease,
   An' dreamin' arl the time o' Plymouth Hoe.
" Take my drum to England, hang et by the shore,
   Strike et when your powder's runnin' low;
If the Dons sight Devon, I'll quit the port o' Heaven,
   An' drum them up the Channel as we drummed them
      long ago."

Drake he's in his hammock till the great Armadas come,
   (Capten, art tha sleepin' there below?),
Slung atween the round shot, listenin' for the drum,
   An' dreamin' arl the time o' Plymouth Hoe.
Call him on the deep sea, call him up the Sound,
   Call him when ye sail to meet the foe;
Where the old trade's plyin' an' the old flag flyin'
   They shall find him ware an' wakin', as they found
      him long ago!

                   SIR HENRY NEWBOLT

THE SAILOR'S CONSOLATION

One night came on a hurricane,
   The sea was mountains rolling,
When Barney Buntline slewed his quid
   And said to Billy Bowline:
" A strong nor'-wester's blowing, Bill:
   Hark! don't ye hear it roar now?
Lord help 'em, how I pities them
   Unhappy folks on shore now.

" Foolhardy chaps as live in towns,
   What danger they are all in,
And now lie quaking in their beds,
   For fear the roof should fall in!
Poor creatures, how they envies us
   And wishes, I've a notion,
For our good luck in such a storm
   To be upon the ocean!

" And as for them that's out all day
   On business from their houses,
And late at night returning home
   To cheer their babes and spouses;
While you and I, Bill, on the deck
   Are comfortably lying,
My eyes! what tiles and chimney-pots
   About their heads are flying!

" Both you and I have oft-times heard
   How men are killed and undone

By overturns from carriages,
　By thieves and fires, in London.
We know what risks these landsmen run,
　From noblemen to tailors;
Then, Bill, let us thank Providence
　That you and I are sailors."

CHARLES DIBDIN

THE OLD NAVY

The captain stood on the carronade[1]: " First lieutenant,"
　says he,
" Send all my merry men aft here, for they must list
　to me;
I haven't the gift of the gab, my sons—because I'm bred
　to the sea;
That ship there is a Frenchman, who means to fight
　with we.
　　And odds bobs, hammer and tongs, long as I've
　　　been to sea,
　　I've fought 'gainst every odds—and I've gained
　　　the victory!

" That ship there is a Frenchman, and if we don't
　take she,
'Tis a thousand bullets to one, that she will capture we;
I haven't the gift of the gab, my boys; so each man
　to his gun;
If she's not mine in half an hour, I'll flog each mother's
　son.

　　　　　　[1] Naval gun first cast at Carron, near Edinburgh.

For odds bobs, hammer and tongs, long as I've
been to sea,
I've fought 'gainst every odds—and I've gained
the victory! "

We fought for twenty minutes, when the Frenchman
had enough;
" I little thought," said he, " that your men were of such
stuff ":
Our captain took the Frenchman's sword, a low bow
made to he;
" I haven't the gift of the gab, monsieur, but polite I
wish to be.
And odds bobs, hammer and tongs, long as I've
been to sea,
I've fought 'gainst every odds—and I've gained
the victory! "

Our captain sent for all of us: " My merry men," said
he,
" I haven't the gift of the gab, my lads, but yet I
thankful be:
You've done your duty handsomely, each man stood
to his gun;
If you hadn't, you villains, as sure as day, I'd have
flogged each mother's son,
For odds bobs, hammer and tongs, as long as
I'm at sea,
I'll fight 'gainst every odds—and I'll gain the
victory! "

FREDERICK MARRYAT

234

AWAY, HAUL AWAY[1]

Away, haul away, boys, haul away together,
  Away, haul away, boys, haul away O;
Away, haul away, boys, haul away together,
  Away, haul away, boys, haul away O.

Louis was the King of France afore the Revoluti—on,
  Away, haul away, boys, haul away O;
Louis was the King of France afore the Revoluti—on,
  Away, haul away, boys, haul away O.

But Louis got his head cut off, which spoiled his
    con—stitu—ti—on,
  Away, haul away, boys, haul away O;
But Louis got his head cut off, which spoiled his
    con—sti—tu—tion,
  Away, haul away, boys, haul away O.

ANONYMOUS

SPANISH WATERS

Spanish waters, Spanish waters, you are ringing in my
    ears,
Like a slow sweet piece of music from the grey forgotten
    years;
Telling tales, and beating tunes, and bringing weary
    thoughts to me
Of the sandy beach at Muertos, where I would that I
    could be.

[1] A Sea Chanty for hauling up sails or tautening the bowlines.

There's a surf breaks on Los Muertos, and it never stops
    to roar,
And it's there we came to anchor, and it's there we went
    ashore,
Where the blue lagoon is silent amid snags of rotting
    trees,
Dropping like the clothes of corpses cast up by the seas.

We anchored at Los Muertos when the dipping sun was
    red,
We left her half-a-mile to sea, to west of Nigger Head;
And before the mist was on the Cay, before the day was
    done,
We were all ashore on Muertos with the gold that we
    had won.

We bore it through the marshes in a half-score battered
    chests,
Sinking, in the sucking quagmires, to the sunburn on
    our breasts,
Heaving over tree-trunks, gasping, damning at the flies
    and heat,
Longing for a long drink, out of silver, in the ship's cool
    lazareet.[1]

The moon came white and ghostly as we laid the
    treasure down,
There was gear there'd make a beggar man as rich as
    Lima Town,
Copper charms and silver trinkets from the chests of
    Spanish crews,
Gold doubloons and double moidores, louis d'ors and
    portagues,

[1] A place between decks on the fore part of a ship.

Clumsy yellow-metal earrings from the Indians of
    Brazil,
Uncut emeralds out of Rio, bezoar stones[1] from
    Guayaquil;
Silver, in the crude and fashioned, pots of old Arica
    bronze,
Jewels from the bones of Incas desecrated by the Dons.

We smoothed the place with mattocks, and we took and
    blazed the tree,
Which marks yon where the gear is hid that none will
    ever see,
And we laid aboard the ship again, and south away we
    steers,
Through the loud surf of Los Muertos which is beating
    in my ears.

I'm the last alive that knows it. All the rest have gone
    their ways,
Killed, or died, or come to anchor in the old Mulatas
    Cays,
And I go singing, fiddling, old and starved and in
    despair,
And I know where all that gold is hid, if I were only
    there.

It's not the way to end it all. I'm old, and nearly blind,
And an old man's past's a strange thing, for it never
    leaves his mind.
And I see in dreams, awhiles, the beach, the sun's disc
    dipping red,
And the tall ship, under topsails, swaying in past Nigger
    Head.

[1] Stones acting as antidotes.

I'd be glad to step ashore there. Glad to take a pick
    and go
To the lone blazed coco-palm tree in the place no others
    know,
And lift the gold and silver that has mouldered there
    for years
By the loud surf of Los Muertos which is beating in my
    ears.

JOHN MASEFIELD

FLANNAN ISLE

" Though three men dwell on Flannan Isle
To keep the lamp alight,
As we steer'd under the lee, we caught
No glimmer through the night! "

A passing ship at dawn had brought
The news; and quickly we set sail,
To find out what strange thing might ail
The keepers of the deep-sea light.

The winter day broke blue and bright,
With glancing sun and glancing spray,
As o'er the swell our boat made way,
As gallant as a gull in flight.

But, as we near'd the lonely Isle;
And look'd up at the naked height;
And saw the lighthouse towering white,
With blinded lantern, that all night

238

Had never shot a spark
Of comfort through the dark,
So ghostly in the cold sunlight
It seem'd, that we were struck the while
With wonder all too deep for words.

And, as into the tiny creek
We stole beneath the hanging crag,
We saw three queer, black, ugly birds—
Too big, by far, in my belief,
For guillemot or shag—
Like seamen sitting bolt-upright
Upon a half-tide reef:
But, as we near'd, they plunged from sight,
Without a sound, or spurt of white.

And still too mazed to speak,
We landed; and made fast the boat;
And climb'd the track in single file,
Each wishing he was safe afloat,
On any sea, however far,
So it be far from Flannan Isle:
And still we seem'd to climb, and climb,
As though we'd lost all count of time,
And so must climb for evermore.
Yet, all too soon, we reached the door—
The black, sun-blister'd lighthouse-door,
That gaped for us ajar.

As, on the threshold, for a spell,
We paused, we seem'd to breathe the smell
Of limewash and of tar,
Familiar as our daily breath,

239

As though 'twere some strange scent of death:
And so, yet wondering, side by side,
We stood a moment, still tongue-tied:
And each with black foreboding eyed
The door, ere we should fling it wide,
To leave the sunlight for the gloom:
Till, plucking courage up, at last,
Hard on each other's heels we pass'd
Into the living-room.

Yet, as we crowded through the door,
We only saw a table, spread
For dinner, meat and cheese and bread;
But all untouch'd; and no one there:
As though, when they sat down to eat,
Ere they could even taste,
Alarm had come; and they in haste
Had risen and left the bread and meat:
For at the table-head a chair
Lay tumbled on the floor.
We listen'd; but we only heard
The feeble cheeping of a bird
That starved upon its perch:
And, listening still, without a word,
We set about our hopeless search.

We hunted high, we hunted low,
And soon ransack'd the empty house;
Then o'er the Island, to and fro,
We ranged, to listen and to look
In every cranny, cleft or nook
That might have hid a bird or mouse:

But, though we search'd from shore to shore,
We found no sign in any place:
And soon again stood face to face
Before the gaping door:
And stole into the room once more
As frighten'd children steal.

Aye: though we hunted high and low,
And hunted everywhere,
Of the three men's fate we found no trace
Of any kind in any place,
But a door ajar, and an untouch'd meal,
And an overtoppled chair.

And, as we listen'd in the gloom
Of that forsaken living-room—
A chill clutch on our breath—
We thought how ill-chance came to all
Who kept the Flannan Light:
And how the rock had been the death
Of many a likely lad:

How six had come to a sudden end,
And three had gone stark mad:
And one whom we'd all known as friend
Had leapt from the lantern one still night,
And fallen dead by the lighthouse wall:
And long we thought
On the three we sought,
And of what might yet befall.

Like curs a glance has brought to heel,
We listen'd, flinching there:

And look'd, and look'd, on the untouch'd meal
And the overtoppled chair.

We seem'd to stand for an endless while,
Though still no word was said,
Three men alive on Flannan Isle,
Who thought on three men dead.

WILFRID WILSON GIBSON

THE RIME OF THE ANCIENT MARINER

PART I

It is an ancient Mariner,
And he stoppeth one of three.
—" By thy long grey beard and glittering
    eye,
Now wherefore stopp'st thou me?

An ancient Mariner meeteth three Gallants bidden to a wedding-feast, and detaineth one.

" The Bridegroom's doors are opened wide,
And I am next of kin;
The guests are met, the feast is set :
May'st hear the merry din."

He holds him with his skinny hand;
" There was a ship," quoth he.
—" Hold off! unhand me, grey-beard loon! "
Eftsoons his hand dropt he.

He holds him with his glittering eye—
The Wedding-Guest stood still,
And listens like a three years' child :
The Mariner hath his will.

The Wedding-Guest is spellbound by the eye of the old sea-faring man, and constrained to hear his tale.

The Wedding-Guest sat on a stone;
He cannot choose but hear;
And thus spake on that ancient man,
The bright-eyed Mariner.

" The ship was cheered, the harbour cleared,
Merrily did we drop
Below the kirk, below the hill,
Below the lighthouse top.

" The Sun came up upon the left,
Out of the sea came he!
And he shone bright, and on the right,
Went down into the sea.

The Mariner tells how the ship sailed southward with a good wind and fair weather, till it reached the Line.

" Higher and higher every day,
Till over the mast at noon "—
The Wedding-Guest here beat his breast,
For he heard the loud bassoon.

The bride hath paced into the hall,
Red as a rose is she;
Nodding their heads before her goes
The merry minstrelsy.

The Wedding-Guest heareth the bridal music; but the Mariner continueth his tale.

The Wedding-Guest he beat his breast,
Yet he cannot choose but hear;
And thus spake on that ancient man,
The bright-eyed Mariner.

" And now the storm-blast came, and he
Was tyrannous and strong:
He struck with his o'ertaking wings,
And chased us south along.

The ship drawn by a storm toward the south pole.

243

" With sloping masts and dipping prow,
As who pursued with yell and blow
Still treads the shadow of his foe,
And forward bends his head,
The ship drove fast, loud roared the blast,
And southward aye we fled.

" And now there came both mist and snow,
And it grew wondrous cold:
And ice, mast-high, came floating by,
As green as emerald.

"And through the drifts the snowy clifts
Did send a dismal sheen:
Nor shapes of men nor beasts we ken—
The ice was all between.

The land of ice, and of fearful sounds, where no living thing was to be seen.

" The ice was here, the ice was there,
The ice was all around:
It cracked and growled, and roared and howled,
Like noises in a swound!

" At length did cross an Albatross,
Thorough the fog it came;
As if it had been a Christian soul,
We hailed it in God's name.

Till a great sea-bird, called the Albatross, came through the snow-fog, and was received with great joy and hospitality.

" It ate the food it ne'er had eat,
And round and round it flew.
The ice did split with a thunder-fit;
The helmsman steered us through!

244

" And a good south wind sprung up
    behind;
The Albatross did follow,
And every day, for food or play,
Came to the mariners' hollo!

And lo! the Albatross proveth a bird of good omen, and followeth the ship, as it returned northward, through fog and floating ice.

" In mist or cloud, on mast or shroud,
It perched for vespers nine;
Whiles all the night, through fog-smoke white,
Glimmered the white moonshine."

" God save thee, ancient Mariner!
From the fiends, that plague thee thus!—
Why look'st thou so? "—" With my cross-bow
I shot the Albatross.

The ancient Mariner inhospitably killeth the pious bird of good omen.

Part II

" The Sun now rose upon the right:
Out of the sea came he,
Still hid in mist—and on the left
Went down into the sea.

" And the good south wind still blew behind,
But no sweet bird did follow,
Nor any day, for food or play,
Came to the mariners' hollo!

" And I had done a hellish thing,
And it would work 'em woe;
For all averred, I had killed the bird
That made the breeze to blow.
' Ah wretch! ' said they, ' the bird to slay,
That made the breeze to blow! '

His shipmates cry out against the ancient Mariner, for killing the bird of good luck.

" Nor dim nor red, like God's own head,
The glorious Sun uprist:
Then all averred, I had killed the bird
That brought the fog and mist.
' 'Twas right,' said they, ' such birds to slay,
That bring the fog and mist.'

But when the fog cleared off, they justify the same, and thus make themselves accomplices in the crime.

" The fair breeze blew, the white foam
     flew,
The furrow followed free;
We were the first that ever burst
Into that silent sea.

The fair breeze continues; the ship enters the Pacific Ocean and sails northward, even till it reaches the Line.

" Down dropt the breeze, the sails dropt
     down,
'Twas sad as sad could be;
And we did speak only to break
The silence of the sea!

The ship hath been suddenly becalmed.

" All in a hot and copper sky,
The bloody Sun, at noon,
Right up above the mast did stand,
No bigger than the Moon.

" Day after day, day after day,
We stuck, nor breath nor motion;
As idle as a painted ship
Upon a painted ocean.

" Water, water, everywhere,
And all the boards did shrink;
Water, water, everywhere,
Nor any drop to drink.

And the Albatross begins to be avenged.

" The very deep did rot: O Christ!
That ever this should be!
Yea, slimy things did crawl with legs
Upon the slimy sea.

" About, about, in reel and rout
The death-fires danced at night;
The water, like a witch's oils,
Burnt green, and blue, and white.

" And some in dreams assurèd were
Of the Spirit that plagued us so;
Nine fathom deep he had followed us
From the land of mist and snow.

A spirit had followed them; one of the invisible inhabitants of this planet, neither departed souls nor angels, concerning whom the learned Jew, Josephus, and the Platonic Constantinopolitan, Michael Psellus, may be consulted. They are very numerous, and there is no climate or element without one or more.

" And every tongue, through utter drought,
Was withered at the root;
We could not speak, no more than if
We had been choked with soot.

" Ah! well a-day! what evil looks
Had I from old and young!
Instead of the cross, the Albatross
About my neck was hung.

The shipmates in their sore distress would fain throw the whole guilt on the ancient Mariner: in sign whereof they hang the dead seabird round his neck.

PART III

" There passed a weary time.   Each throat
Was parched, and glazed each eye.
A weary time! a weary time!
How glazed each weary eye!
When looking westward, I beheld
A something in the sky.

The ancient Mariner beholdeth a sign in the element afar off.

247

'At first it seemed a little speck,
And then it seemed a mist;
It moved and moved, and took at last
A certain shape, I wist.

A speck, a mist, a shape, I wist!
And still it neared and neared:
As if it dodged a water-sprite,
It plunged and tacked and veered.

"With throats unslaked, with black lips baked,
We could not laugh nor wail;
Through utter drought all dumb we stood!
I bit my arm, I sucked the blood,
And cried, 'A sail! a sail!'

At its nearer approach, it seemeth him to be a ship; and at a dear ransom he freeth his speech from the bonds of thirst.

"With throats unslaked, with black lips baked,
Agape they heard me call:
Gramercy! they for joy did grin,
And all at once their breath drew in,
As they were drinking all.

A flash of joy.

"'See! see!' (I cried) 'she tacks no more!
Hither to work us weal;
Without a breeze, without a tide,
She steadies with upright keel!'

And horror follows. For can it be a ship that comes onward without wind or tide?

"The western wave was all a-flame,
The day was well nigh done!
Almost upon the western wave
Rested the broad bright Sun;
When that strange shape drove suddenly
Betwixt us and the Sun.

248

" And straight the Sun was flecked with bars,
(Heaven's Mother send us grace!)
As if through a dungeon-grate he peered
With broad and burning face.

It seemeth him but the skeleton of a ship.

" Alas! (thought I, and my heart beat loud)
How fast she nears and nears!
Are those her sails that glance in the Sun,
Like restless gossameres?

"Are those her ribs through which the Sun
Did peer, as through a grate?
And is that Woman all her crew?
Is that a Death? and are there two?
Is Death that Woman's mate?

And its ribs are seen as bars on the face of the setting Sun. The spectre-woman and her death-mate, and no other on board the skeleton-ship.

" Her lips were red, her looks were free,
Her locks were yellow as gold:
Her skin was as white as leprosy,
The Nightmare Life-in-Death was she,
Who thicks man's blood with cold.

Like vessel, like crew!

" The naked hulk alongside came,
And the twain were casting dice;
'The game is done! I've won! I've won!'
Quoth she, and whistles thrice.

Death and Life-in-Death have diced for the ship's crew, and she (the latter) winneth the ancient Mariner.

" The Sun's rim dips; the stars rush out:
At one stride comes the dark;
With far-heard whisper, o'er the sea,
Off shot the spectre-bark.

No twilight within the courts of the Sun.

" We listened and looked sideways up!
Fear at my heart, as at a cup,
My life-blood seemed to sip!
The stars were dim, and thick the night,
The steersman's face by his lamp gleamed white;
From the sails the dew did drip—
Till clomb above the eastern bar
The hornèd Moon, with one bright star
Within the nether tip.

At the rising of the Moon,

" One after one, by the star-dogged Moon,
Too quick for groan or sigh,
Each turned his face with a ghastly pang,
And cursed me with his eye.

One after another,

" Four times fifty living men
(And I heard nor sigh nor groan),
With heavy thump, a lifeless lump,
They dropt down one by one.

His shipmates drop down dead.

" The souls did from their bodies fly—
They fled to bliss or woe!
And every soul, it passed me by,
Like the whizz of my cross-bow."

But Life-in-Death begins her work on the ancient Mariner.

PART IV

" I fear thee, ancient Mariner!
I fear thy skinny hand!
And thou art long, and lank, and brown,
As is the ribbed sea-sand.

The Wedding-Guest feareth that a spirit is talking to him;

250

" I fear thee and thy glittering eye,
And thy skinny hand so brown."—
" Fear not, fear not, thou Wedding-Guest!
This body dropt not down.

" Alone, alone, all, all alone,
Alone on a wide, wide sea!
And never a saint took pity on
My soul in agony.

" The many men, so beautiful!
And they all dead did lie:
And a thousand thousand slimy things
Lived on; and so did I.

" I looked upon the rotting sea,
And drew my eyes away;
I looked upon the rotting deck,
And there the dead men lay.

" I looked to heaven, and tried to pray;
But or ever a prayer had gusht,
A wicked whisper came, and made
My heart as dry as dust.

" I closed my lids, and kept them close,
And the balls like pulses beat;
For the sky and the sea, and the sea and the sky
Lay like a load on my weary eye,
And the dead were at my feet.

" The cold sweat melted from their limbs,
Nor rot nor reek did they:

The look with which they looked on me
Had never passed away.

" An orphan's curse would drag to Hell
A spirit from on high;
But oh! more horrible than that
Is the curse in a dead man's eye!
Seven days, seven nights, I saw that curse,
And yet I could not die.

" The moving Moon went up the sky,
And nowhere did abide:
Softly she was going up,
And a star or two beside—

In his loneliness and fixedness he yearneth towards the journeying Moon, and the stars that still sojourn, yet still move onward; and everywhere the blue sky belongs to them, and is their appointed rest, and their native country and their own natural homes, which they enter unannounced, as lords that are certainly expected and yet there is a silent joy at their arrival.

" Her beams bemocked the sultry main
Like April hoar-frost spread;
But where the ship's huge shadow lay,
The charmèd water burnt alway
A still and awful red.

" Beyond the shadow of the ship,
I watched the water-snakes:
They moved in tracks of shining white,
And when they reared, the elfish light
Fell off in hoary flakes.

By the light of the Moon he beholdeth God's creatures of the great calm.

" Within the shadow of the ship
I watch'd their rich attire:
Blue, glossy green, and velvet black,
They coiled and swam; and every track
Was a flash of golden fire.

252

" O happy living things! no tongue
Their beauty might declare:
A spring of love gushed from my heart,
And I blessed them unaware:
Sure my kind saint took pity on me,
And I blessed them unaware.

Their beauty and their happiness.

He blesseth them in his heart.

" The selfsame moment I could pray;
And from my neck so free
The Albatross fell off, and sank
Like lead into the sea.

The spell begins to break.

Part V

" O sleep! it is a gentle thing,
Beloved from pole to pole!
To Mary Queen the praise be given!
She sent the gentle sleep from Heaven
That slid into my soul.

" The silly buckets on the deck
That had so long remained,
I dreamt that they were filled with dew;
And when I awoke, it rained.

By grace of the holy Mother, the ancient Mariner is refreshed with rain.

" My lips were wet, my throat was cold,
My garments all were dank;
Sure I had drunken in my dreams,
And still my body drank.

" I moved, and could not feel my limbs:
I was so light—almost
I thought that I had died in sleep,
And was a blessèd ghost.

" And soon I heard a roaring wind:
It did not come anear;
But with its sound it shook the sails,
That were so thin and sere.

He heareth sounds,
and seeth strange
sights and commo-
tions in the sky and
the element.

" The upper air burst into life!
And a hundred fire-flags sheen,
To and fro, they were hurried about;
And to and fro, and in and out,
The wan stars danced between.

" And the coming wind did roar more loud,
And the sails did sigh like sedge;
And the rain poured down from one black cloud;
The Moon was at its edge.

" The thick black cloud was cleft, and still
The Moon was at its side:
Like waters shot from some high crag,
The lightning fell with never a jag,
A river steep and wide.

" The loud wind never reached the ship,
Yet now the ship moved on!
Beneath the lightning and the Moon
The dead men gave a groan.

The bodies of the
ship's crew are in-
spired, and the ship
moves on;

" They groaned, they stirred, they all uprose,
Nor spake, nor moved their eyes;
It had been strange, e'en in a dream,
To have seen those dead men rise.

" The helmsman steered, the ship moved on;
Yet never a breeze up blew;
The mariners all 'gan work the ropes,
Where they were wont to do;
They raised their limbs like lifeless tools—
We were a ghastly crew.

" The body of my brother's son
Stood by me, knee to knee:
The body and I pulled at one rope,
But he said nought to me."

—" I fear thee, ancient Mariner! "
—" Be calm, thou Wedding-Guest!
'Twas not those souls that fled in pain,
Which to their corses came again,
But a troop of spirits blest:

But not by the souls of the men, nor by demons of earth or middle air, but by a blessed troop of angelic spirits, sent down by the invocation of the guardian saint.

" For when it dawned—they dropped their arms,
And clustered round the mast;
Sweet sounds rose slowly through their mouths,
And from their bodies passed.

" Around, around, flew each sweet sound,
Then darted to the Sun;
Slowly the sounds came back again,
Now mixed, now one by one.

" Sometimes a-dropping from the sky
I heard the skylark sing;
Sometimes all little birds that are,
How they seemed to fill the sea and air
With their sweet jargoning!

" And now 'twas like all instruments,
Now like a lonely flute;
And now it is an angel's song,
That makes the heavens be mute.

" It ceased; yet still the sails made on
A pleasant noise till noon,
A noise like of a hidden brook
In the leafy month of June,
That to the sleeping woods all night
Singeth a quiet tune.

" Till noon we quietly sailed on,
Yet never a breeze did breathe:
Slowly and smoothly went the ship,
Moved onward from beneath.

" Under the keel nine fathom deep,
From the land of mist and snow,
The Spirit slid; and it was he
That made the ship to go.
The sails at noon left off their tune,
And the ship stood still also.

The lonesome Spirit
from the South Pole
carries on the ship as
far as the Line, in
obedience to the
angelic troop, but
still requireth
vengeance.

" The Sun, right up above the mast,
Had fixed her to the ocean:

But in a minute she 'gan stir,
With a short uneasy motion—
Backwards and forwards half her length,
With a short uneasy motion.

" Then like a pawing horse let go,
She made a sudden bound :
It flung the blood into my head,
And I fell down in a swound.

" How long in that same fit I lay,
I have not to declare;
But ere my living life returned,
I heard, and in my soul discerned
Two voices in the air.

" ' Is it he? ' quoth one, ' is this the man?
By Him who died on cross,
With his cruel bow he laid full low
The harmless Albatross.

" ' The Spirit who bideth by himself
In the land of mist and snow,
He loved the bird that loved the man
Who shot him with his bow.'

" The other was a softer voice,
As soft as honey-dew :
Quoth he, ' The man hath penance done,
And penance more will do.'

The Polar Spirit's fellow-demons, the invisible inhabitants of the element, take part in his wrong; and two of them relate, one to the other, that penance long and heavy for the ancient Mariner hath been accorded to the Polar Spirit, who returneth southward.

A12

R

Part VI

First Voice

" 'But tell me, tell me! speak again,
Thy soft response renewing—
What makes that ship drive on so fast?
What is the Ocean doing?'

Second Voice

" 'Still as a slave before his lord,
The Ocean hath no blast;
His great bright eye most silently
Up to the Moon is cast—

" 'If he may know which way to go;
For she guides him smooth or grim.
See, brother, see! how graciously
She looketh down on him.'

First Voice

" 'But why drives on that ship so fast,
Without or wave or wind?'

Second Voice

" 'The air is cut away before,
And closes from behind.

" 'Fly, brother, fly! more high, more high!
Or we shall be belated:
For slow and slow that ship will go,
When the Mariner's trance is abated.'

The Mariner hath
been cast into a
trance; for the
angelic power
causeth the vessel to
drive northward
faster than human
life could endure.

" I woke, and we were sailing on
As in a gentle weather:
'Twas night, calm night, the Moon was
    high;
The dead men stood together.

The supernatural
motion is retarded,
the Mariner awakes,
and his penance
begins anew.

" All stood together on the deck,
For a charnel-dungeon fitter:
All fixed on me their stony eyes,
That in the Moon did glitter.

" The pang, the curse, with which they died,
Had never passed away:
I could not draw my eyes from theirs,
Nor turn them up to pray.

" And now this spell was snapt: once more
I viewed the ocean green,
And looked far forth, yet little saw
Of what had else been seen—

The curse is finally
expiated,

" Like one that on a lonesome road
Doth walk in fear and dread,
And having once turned round, walks on,
And turns no more his head;
Because he knows a frightful fiend
Doth close behind him tread.

" But soon there breathed a wind on me,
Nor sound nor motion made:
Its path was not upon the sea,
In ripple or in shade.

"It raised my hair, it fanned my cheek
Like a meadow-gale of spring—
It mingled strangely with my fears,
Yet it felt like a welcoming.

"Swiftly, swiftly flew the ship,
Yet she sailed softly too:
Sweetly, sweetly blew the breeze—
On me alone it blew.

"Oh! dream of joy! is this indeed
The lighthouse top I see?
Is this the hill? is this the kirk?
Is this mine own countree?

And the ancient
Mariner beholdeth
his native country.

"We drifted o'er the harbour-bar,
And I with sobs did pray—
O let me be awake, my God!
Or let me sleep alway.

"The harbour-bay was clear as glass,
So smoothly it was strewn!
And on the bay the moonlight lay,
And the shadow of the Moon.

"The rock shone bright, the kirk no less,
That stands above the rock:
The moonlight steeped in silentness
The steady weathercock.

"And the bay was white with silent light,
Till, rising from the same,

Full many shapes, that shadows were,
In crimson colours came.

The angelic spirits
leave the dead
bodies,

" A little distance from the prow
Those crimson shadows were :
I turned my eyes upon the deck—
O Christ! what saw I there!

And appear in their
own forms of light

" Each corse lay flat, lifeless and flat,
And, by the holy rood!
A man all light, a seraph-man,
On every corse there stood.

" This seraph-band, each waved his hand :
It was a heavenly sight!
They stood as signals to the land,
Each one a lovely light :

" This seraph-band, each waved his hand,
No voice did they impart—
No voice; but oh! the silence sank
Like music on my heart.

" But soon I heard the dash of oars,
I heard the Pilot's cheer;
My head was turned perforce away,
And I saw a boat appear.

" The Pilot and the Pilot's boy,
I heard them coming fast :
Dear Lord in Heaven! it was a joy
The dead men could not blast.

" I saw a third—I heard his voice:
It is the Hermit good!
He singeth loud his godly hymns
That he makes in the wood.
He'll shrieve my soul, he'll wash away
The Albatross's blood.

Part VII

" This Hermit good lives in that wood
Which slopes down to the sea.
How loudly his sweet voice he rears!
He loves to talk with marineres
That come from a far countree.

The Hermit of the Wood

" He kneels at morn, and noon, and eve—
He hath a cushion plump:
It is the moss that wholly hides
The rotted old oak-stump.

" The skiff-boat neared: I heard them talk,
' Why, this is strange, I trow!
Where are those lights so many and fair,
That signal made but now? '

" ' Strange, by my faith,' the Hermit
        said—
' And they answered not our cheer!
The planks look warped! and see those sails,
How thin they are and sere!
I never saw aught like to them,
Unless perchance it were

Approacheth the ship with wonder.

" ' Brown skeletons of leaves that lag
My forest-brook along;
When the ivy-tod is heavy with snow,
And the owlet whoops to the wolf below,
That eats the she-wolf's young.'

" ' Dear Lord! it hath a fiendish look '—
(The Pilot made reply)
' I am a-feared.'—' Push on, push on! '
Said the Hermit cheerily.

" The boat came closer to the ship,
But I nor spake nor stirred;
The boat came close beneath the ship,
And straight a sound was heard.

" Under the water it rumbled on,
Still louder and more dread:
It reached the ship, it split the bay;
The ship went down like lead.

The ship suddenly sinketh.

" Stunned by that loud and dreadful sound,
Which sky and ocean smote,
Like one that hath been seven days drowned
My body lay afloat;
But swift as dreams, myself I found
Within the Pilot's boat.

The ancient Mariner is saved in the Pilot's boat.

" Upon the whirl, where sank the ship,
The boat spun round and round;
And all was still, save that the hill
Was telling of the sound.

"I moved my lips—the Pilot shrieked
And fell down in a fit;
The holy Hermit raised his eyes,
And prayed where he did sit.

"I took the oars: the Pilot's boy,
Who now doth crazy go,
Laughed loud and long, and all the while
His eyes went to and fro.
'Ha! ha!' quoth he, 'full plain I see
The Devil knows how to row.'

"And now, all in my own countree,
I stood on the firm land!
The Hermit stepped forth from the boat,
And scarcely he could stand.

"'O shrieve me, shrieve me, holy man!'
The Hermit crossed his brow,
'Say quick,' quoth he, 'I bid thee say—
What manner of man art thou?'

The ancient Mariner
earnestly entreateth
the Hermit to shrieve
him; and the penance
of life falls on him.

"Forthwith this frame of mine was wrenched
With a woful agony,
Which forced me to begin my tale;
And then it left me free.

"Since then, at an uncertain hour,
That agony returns:
And till my ghastly tale is told,
This heart within me burns.

And ever and anon
throughout his future
life an agony con-
straineth him to
travel from land to
land;

264

" I pass, like night, from land to land;
I have strange power of speech;
That moment that his face I see,
I know the man that must hear me:
To him my tale I teach.

" What loud uproar bursts from that door!
The wedding-guests are there:
But in the garden-bower the bride
And bridesmaids singing are:
And hark, the little vesper bell,
Which biddeth me to prayer!

" O Wedding-Guest! this soul hath been
Alone on a wide, wide sea;
So lonely 'twas, that God Himself
Scarce seemèd there to be.

" O sweeter than the marriage-feast,
'Tis sweeter far to me,
To walk together to the kirk
With a goodly company!—

" To walk together to the kirk,
And all together pray,
While each to his great Father bends,
Old men, and babes, and loving friends,
And youths and maidens gay!

" Farewell, farewell! but this I tell
To thee, thou Wedding-Guest!
He prayeth well, who loveth well
Both man and bird and beast.

And to teach by his own example, love and reverence to all things that God made and loveth.

" He prayeth best, who loveth best
All things both great and small;
For the dear God who loveth us,
He made and loveth all."

The Mariner, whose eye is bright,
Whose beard with age is hoar,
Is gone: and now the Wedding-Guest
Turned from the bridegroom's door.

He went like one that hath been stunned,
And is of sense forlorn:
A sadder and a wiser man,
He rose the morrow morn.

SAMUEL TAYLOR COLERIDGE

OUT OF DOORS

THE FOOTPATH WAY

Jog on, jog on, the footpath way,
  And merrily hent the stile-a:
A merry heart goes all the day,
  Your sad tires in a mile-a.

WILLIAM SHAKESPEARE

THE OLD SQUIRE

I like the hunting of the hare
  Better than that of the fox;
I like the joyous morning air,
  And the crowing of the cocks.

I like the calm of the early fields,
  The ducks asleep by the lake,
The quiet hour which Nature yields,
  Before mankind is awake.

I like the pheasants and feeding things
  Of the unsuspicious morn;
I like the flap of the wood-pigeon's wings
  As she rises from the corn.

I like the blackbird's shriek, and his rush
　　From the turnips as I pass by,
And the partridge hiding her head in a bush,
　　For her young ones cannot fly.

I like these things, and I like to ride
　　When all the world is in bed,
To the top of the hill where the sky grows wide,
　　And where the sun grows red.

The beagles at my horse heels trot
　　In silence after me;
There's Ruby, Roger, Diamond, Dot,
　　Old Slut and Margery,—

A score of names well-used and dear,
　　The names my childhood knew;
The horn, with which I rouse their cheer,
　　Is the horn my father blew.

I like the hunting of the hare
　　Better than that of the fox;
The new world still is all less fair
　　Than the old world it mocks.

I covet not a wider range
　　Than these dear manors give;
I take my pleasures without change,
　　And as I lived I live.

I leave my neighbours to their thought;
　　My choice it is, and pride,

On my own lands to find my sport,
    In my own fields to ride.

The hare herself no better loves
    The field where she was bred
Than I the habit of these groves,
    My own inherited.

I know my quarries every one,
    The meuse[1] where she sits low;
The road she chose to-day was run
    A hundred years ago.

The lags, the gills, the forest ways,
    The hedgerows one and all,
These are the kingdoms of my chase,
    And bounded by my wall;

Nor has the world a better thing,
    Though one should search it round
Than thus to live one's own sole king,
    Upon one's own sole ground.

I like the hunting of the hare;
    It brings me, day by day,
The memory of old days as fair,
    With dead men past away.

To these, as homeward still I ply
    And pass the churchyard gate
Where all are laid as I must lie,
    I stop and raise my hat.

[1] A gap in a hedge through which a hare can escape.

I like the hunting of the hare;
New sports I hold in scorn.
I like to be as my fathers were
In the days ere I was born.

WILFRID SCAWEN BLUNT

TEWKESBURY ROAD

It is good to be out on the road, and going one knows
not where,
Going through meadow and village, one knows not
whither nor why;
Through the grey light drift of the dust, in the keen
cool rush of the air,
Under the flying white clouds, and the broad blue lift
of the sky;

And to halt at the chattering brook, in the tall green
fern at the brink
Where the harebell grows, and the gorse, and the
foxgloves purple and white;
Where the shy-eyed delicate deer troop down to the
pools to drink,
When the stars are mellow and large at the coming
on of the night.

O! to feel the warmth of the rain, and the homely
smell of the earth,
Is a tune for the blood to jig to, a joy past power of
words;

And the blessed green comely meadows seem all a-ripple
    with mirth
  At the lilt of the shifting feet, and the dear wild cry
    of the birds.

JOHN MASEFIELD

WEATHERS

This is the weather the cuckoo likes,
    And so do I;
When showers betumble the chestnut spikes,
    And nestlings fly:
And the little brown nightingale bills his best,
And they sit outside at "The Travellers'
    Rest,"
And maids come forth sprig-muslin drest,
And citizens dream of the south and west,
    And so do I.

This is the weather the shepherd shuns,
    And so do I;
When beeches drip on browns and duns,
    And thresh, and ply;
And hill-hid tides throb, throe on throe,
And meadow rivulets overflow,
And drops on gate-bars hang in a row,
And rooks in families homeward go,
    And so do I.

THOMAS HARDY

ODE TO THE NORTH-EAST WIND

Welcome, wild North-easter!
  Shame it is to see
Odes to every zephyr;
  Ne'er a verse to thee.
Welcome, black North-easter!
  O'er the German foam;
O'er the Danish moorlands,
  From thy frozen home.
Tired we are of summer,
  Tired of gaudy glare,
Showers soft and steaming,
  Hot and breathless air.
Tired of listless dreaming,
  Through the lazy day:
Jovial wind of winter,
  Turn us out to play!
Sweep the golden reed-beds;
  Crisp the lazy dyke;
Hunger into madness
  Every plunging pike.
Fill the lake with wild-fowl;
  Fill the marsh with snipe;
While on dreary moorlands
  Lonely curlew pipe.
Through the black fir-forest
  Thunder harsh and dry,
Shattering down the snow-flakes
  Off the curdled sky.

Hark!   The brave North-easter!
  Breast-high lies the scent,
On by holt[1] and headland,
  Over heath and bent.[2]
Chime, ye dappled darlings,
  Through the sleet and snow.
Who can over-ride you?
  Let the horses go!
Chime, ye dappled darlings,
  Down the roaring blast;
You shall see a fox die
  Ere an hour be past.
Go! and rest to-morrow,
  Hunting in your dreams,
While our skates are ringing
  O'er the frozen streams.
Let the luscious South-wind
  Breathe in lovers' sighs,
While the lazy gallants
  Bask in ladies' eyes.
What does he but soften
  Heart alike and pen?
'Tis the hard grey weather
  Breeds hard English men.
What's the soft South-wester?
  'Tis the ladies' breeze,
Bringing home their true loves
  Out of all the seas:
But the black North-easter,
  Through the snowstorm hurled,

---

[1] Wood.   [2] Stiff, grass-like reeds.

Drives our English hearts of oak
    Seaward round the world.
Come, as came our fathers,
    Heralded by thee,
Conquering from the eastward,
    Lords by land and sea.
Come; and strong within us
    Stir the Vikings' blood;
Bracing brain and sinew;
    Blow, thou wind of God!

CHARLES KINGSLEY

A FINE DAY

Clear had the day been from the dawn,
    All chequered was the sky,
Thin clouds like scarfs of cobweb lawn
    Veiled heaven's most glorious eye.
The wind had no more strength than this,
    That leisurely it blew,
To make one leaf the next to kiss
    That closely by it grew.

MICHAEL DRAYTON

THE WINDMILL

The green corn waving in the dale,
The ripe grass waving on the hill:
I lean across the paddock pale
And gaze upon the giddy mill.

Its hurtling sails a mighty sweep
Cut thro' the air: with rushing sound
Each strikes in fury down the steep,
Rattles, and whirls in chase around.

Beside his sacks the miller stands
On high within the open door:
A book and pencil in his hands,
His grist and meal he reckoneth o'er.

His tireless merry slave, the wind,
Is busy with his work to-day:
From whencesoe'er he comes to grind;
He hath a will and knows the way.

He gives the creaking sails a spin,
The circling millstones faster flee,
The shuddering timbers groan within,
And down the shoot the meal runs free.

The miller giveth him no thanks,
And doth not much his work o'erlook:
He stands beside the sacks, and ranks
The figures in his dusty book.

ROBERT BRIDGES

UNDER THE GREENWOOD TREE

Under the greenwood tree
Who loves to lie with me,
And turn his merry note
Unto the sweet bird's throat—

Come hither, come hither, come hither!
    Here shall he see
    No enemy
But winter and rough weather.

    Who doth ambition shun
    And loves to live i' the sun,
    Seeking the food he eats
    And pleased with what he gets—
Come hither, come hither, come hither!
    Here shall he see
    No enemy
But winter and rough weather.

WILLIAM SHAKESPEARE

ORPHEUS WITH HIS LUTE

Orpheus with his lute made trees
And the mountain tops that freeze
    Bow themselves, when he did sing:
To his music plants and flowers
Ever sprung; as sun and showers
    There had made a lasting spring.

Every thing that heard him play,
Even the billows of the sea,
    Hung their heads, and then lay by.
In sweet music is such art,
Killing care and grief of heart
    Fall asleep, or hearing, die.

WILLIAM SHAKESPEARE

THE ANGLER'S SONG

As inward love breeds outward talk,
The hound some praise, and some the
    hawk;
Some, better pleased with private sport,
Use tennis; some a mistress court:
  But these delights I neither wish,
  Nor envy, while I freely fish.

Who hunts, doth oft in danger ride;
Who hawks, lures oft both far and wide;
Who uses games, shall often prove
A loser; but who falls in love
  Is fettered in fond Cupid's snare:
  My angle breeds me no such care.

Of recreation there is none
So free as fishing is alone;
All other pastimes do no less
Than mind and body both possess;
  My hand alone my work can do,
  So I can fish and study too.

I care not, I, to fish in seas—
Fresh rivers best my mind do please,
Whose sweet calm course I contemplate,
And seek in life to imitate:
  In civil bounds I fain would keep,
  And for my past offences weep.

And when the timorous trout I wait
To take, and he devours my bait,
How poor a thing, sometimes I find,
Will captivate a greedy mind;
   And when none bite, I praise the wise,
   Whom vain allurements ne'er surprise.

But yet, though while I fish I fast,
I make good fortune my repast;
And thereunto my friend invite,
In whom I more than that delight:
   Who is more welcome to my dish
   Than to my angle was my fish.

As well content no prize to take,
As use of taken prize to make:
For so our Lord was pleasèd, when
He fishers made fishèrs of men;
   Where, which is in no other game,
   A man may fish and praise His name.

The first men that our Saviour dear
Did choose to wait upon Him here,
Blest fishers were, and fish the last
Food was that He on earth did taste:
   I therefore strive to follow those
   Whom He to follow Him hath chose.

IZAAK WALTON

THE SOLITARY REAPER

Behold her, single in the field,
  Yon solitary Highland Lass!
Reaping and singing by herself;
  Stop here, or gently pass!
Alone she cuts and binds the grain,
And sings a melancholy strain;
O listen! for the vale profound
Is overflowing with the sound.

No nightingale did ever chaunt
  More welcome notes to weary bands
Of travellers in some shady haunt,
  Among Arabian sands:
A voice so thrilling ne'er was heard
In spring-time from the Cuckoo-bird,
Breaking the silence of the seas
Among the farthest Hebrides.

Will no one tell me what she sings?—
  Perhaps the plaintive numbers flow
For old, unhappy, far-off things,
  And battles long ago:
Or is it some more humble lay,
Familiar matter of to-day?
Some natural sorrow, loss, or pain,
That has been, and may be again?

Whate'er the theme, the maiden sang
  As if her song could have no ending;

I saw her singing at her work,
 And o'er the sickle bending;—
I listen'd, motionless and still;
And, as I mounted up the hill,
The music in my heart I bore
Long after it was heard no more.

WILLIAM WORDSWORTH

WESTMINSTER BRIDGE

Earth has not anything to show more fair:
Dull would he be of soul who could pass by
A sight so touching in its majesty:
This City now doth like a garment wear
The beauty of the morning; silent, bare,
Ships, towers, domes, theatres, and temples lie
Open unto the fields, and to the sky;
All bright and glittering in the smokeless air.
Never did sun more beautifully steep
In his first splendour, valley, rock, or hill;
Ne'er saw I, never felt, a calm so deep!
The river glideth at his own sweet will:
Dear God! the very houses seem asleep;
And all that mighty heart is lying still!

WILLIAM WORDSWORTH

BIRDS AND BEASTS

TO THE CUCKOO

O blithe New-comer! I have heard,
I hear thee and rejoice.
O Cuckoo! shall I call thee Bird,
Or but a wandering Voice?

While I am lying on the grass
Thy twofold shout I hear;
From hill to hill it seems to pass,
At once far off, and near.

Though babbling only to the vale
Of sunshine and of flowers,
Thou bringest unto me a tale
Of visionary hours.

Thrice welcome, darling of the Spring!
Even yet thou art to me
No bird, but an invisible thing,
A voice, a mystery;

The same whom in my schoolboy days
I listened to; that Cry

Which made me look a thousand ways
In bush, and tree, and sky.

To seek thee did I often rove
Through woods and on the green;
And thou wert still a hope, a love;
Still longed for, never seen.

And I can listen to thee yet;
Can lie upon the plain
And listen, till I do beget
That golden time again.

O blessèd Bird! the earth we pace
Again appears to be
An unsubstantial, faery place,
That is fit home for Thee!

WILLIAM WORDSWORTH

THE SNARE

I hear a sudden cry of pain!
    There is a rabbit in a snare:
Now I hear the cry again,
    But I cannot tell from where.

But I cannot tell from where
    He is calling out for aid;
Crying on the frightened air,
    Making everything afraid.

Making everything afraid,
 Wrinkling up his little face,
As he cries again for aid;
 And I cannot find the place!

And I cannot find the place
 Where his paw is in the snare:
Little one! Oh, little one!
 I am searching everywhere.

JAMES STEPHENS

THE EAGLE

He clasps the crag with crookèd hands;
Close to the sun in lonely lands,
Ring'd with the azure world, he stands.

The wrinkled sea beneath him crawls;
He watches from his mountain walls,
And like a thunderbolt he falls.

LORD TENNYSON

THE DONKEY

When fishes flew and forests walked
 And figs grew upon thorn,
Some moment when the moon was blood
 Then surely I was born;

With monstrous head and sickening cry
  And ears like errant wings,
The devil's walking parody
  On all four-footed things.

The tattered outlaw of the earth,
  Of ancient crooked will;
Starve, scourge, deride me: I am dumb,
  I keep my secret still.

Fools! For I also had my hour;
  One far fierce hour and sweet:
There was a shout about my ears,
  And palms before my feet.

GILBERT KEITH CHESTERTON

THE TIGER

Tiger, tiger, burning bright
In the forests of the night,
What immortal hand or eye
Could frame thy fearful symmetry?

In what distant deeps or skies
Burnt the fire of thine eyes?
On what wings dare he aspire—
What the hand dare seize the fire?

And what shoulder, and what art,
Could twist the sinews of thy heart?
And, when thy heart began to beat,
What dread hand, and what dread feet?

What the hammer? what the chain?
In what furnace was thy brain?
What the anvil? what dread grasp
Dare its deadly terrors clasp?

When the stars threw down their spears,
And watered heaven with their tears,
Did He smile His work to see?
Did He who made the lamb make thee?

Tiger, tiger, burning bright
In the forests of the night,
What immortal hand or eye
Dare frame thy fearful symmetry?

WILLIAM BLAKE

THE THRUSH'S NEST

Within a thick and spreading hawthorn bush,
   That overhung a molehill large and round,
I heard from morn to morn a merry thrush
   Sing hymns to sunrise, and I drank the sound
With joy; and, often an intruding guest,
   I watched her secret toils from day to day—
How true she warped the moss to form a nest,
   And modelled it within with wood and clay;
And by and by, like heath-bells gilt with dew,
   There lay her shining eggs, as bright as flowers,
Ink-spotted over shells of greeny blue;
   And there I witnessed, in the sunny hours,
A brood of Nature's minstrels chirp and fly,
Glad as that sunshine and the laughing sky.

JOHN CLARE

DUCKS

I

From troubles of the world
I turn to ducks,
Beautiful comical things
Sleeping or curled
Their heads beneath white wings
By water cool,
Or finding curious things
To eat in various mucks
Beneath the pool,
Tails uppermost, or waddling
Sailor-like on the shores
Of ponds, or paddling
—Left! right!—with fanlike feet
Which are for steady oars
When they (white galleys) float
Each bird a boat
Rippling at will the sweet
Wide waterway. . . .
When night is fallen *you* creep
Upstairs, but drakes and dillies
Nest with pale water-stars,
Moonbeams and shadow bars,
And water-lilies:
Fearful too much to sleep
Since they've no locks
To click against the teeth
Of weasel and fox.

286

And warm beneath
Are eggs of cloudy green
Whence hungry rats and lean
Would stealthily suck
New life, but for the mien,
The bold ferocious mien
Of the mother-duck.

II

Yes, ducks are valiant things
On nests of twigs and straws,
And ducks are soothy things
And lovely on the lake
When that the sunlight draws
Thereon their pictures dim
In colours cool.
And when beneath the pool
They dabble, and when they swim
And make their rippling rings,
O ducks are beautiful things!

But ducks are comical things:—
As comical as you.
Quack!
They waddle round, they do.
They eat all sorts of things.
And then they quack.
By barn and stable and stack
They wander at their will,
But if you go too near
They look at you through black
Small topaz-tinted eyes

And wish you ill.
Triangular and clear
They leave their curious track
In mud at the water's edge,
And there amid the sedge
And slime they gobble and peer
Saying " Quack! quack! "

III

When God had finished the stars and whirl of coloured
        suns
He turned His mind from big things to fashion little
        ones,
Beautiful tiny things (like daisies) He made, and then
He made the comical ones in case the minds of men
        Should stiffen and become
        Dull, humourless and glum :
And so forgetful of their Maker be
As to take even themselves—*quite seriously*.
Caterpillars and cats are lively and excellent puns :
All God's jokes are good—even the practical ones!
And as for the duck, I think God must have smiled a bit
Seeing those eyes blink on the day He fashioned it.
And He's probably laughing still at the sound that came
        out of its bill!

F. W. HARVEY

TWILIGHT TO SUNRISE

THE FALLING NIGHT

Shepherds all, and maidens fair,
Fold your flocks up, for the air
'Gins to thicken, and the sun
Already his great course hath run.
See the dew-drops, how they kiss
Every little flower that is.
Hanging on their velvet heads,
Like a rope of crystal beads:
See the heavy clouds low falling,
And bright Hesperus down calling
The dead Night from under ground;
At whose rising, mists unsound,
Damps and vapours fly apace,
Hovering o'er the wanton face
Of these pastures, where they come,
Striking dead both bud and bloom:
Therefore, from such danger lock
Every one his lovèd flock;
And let your dogs lie loose without,
Lest the wolf come as a scout
From the mountain, and ere day,
Bear a lamb or kid away;

Or the crafty thievish fox
Break upon your simple flocks.
To secure yourselves from these,
Be not too secure in ease;
Let one eye his watches keep,
Whilst the other eye doth sleep;
So you shall good shepherds prove,
And for ever hold the love
Of our great god.   Sweetest slumbers,
And soft silence fall in numbers
On your eyelids!   So, farewell!
Thus I end my evening's knell.

JOHN FLETCHER

THE SPLENDOUR FALLS ON CASTLE WALLS

The splendour falls on castle walls
    And snowy summits old in story:
The long light shakes across the lakes,
    And the wild cataract leaps in glory.
Blow, bugle, blow, set the wild echoes flying,
Blow, bugle; answer, echoes, dying, dying, dying.

O hark, O hear! how thin and clear,
    And thinner, clearer, farther going!
O sweet and far from cliff and scar
    The horns of Elfland faintly blowing!
Blow, let us hear the purple glens replying:
Blow, bugle; answer, echoes, dying, dying, dying.

O love, they die in yon rich sky,
    They faint on hill or field or river:
Our echoes roll from soul to soul,
    And grow for ever and for ever.
Blow, bugle, blow, set the wild echoes flying,
And answer, echoes, answer, dying, dying, dying.

                        LORD TENNYSON

SILVER

Slowly, silently, now the moon
Walks the night in her silver shoon;
This way, and that, she peers, and sees
Silver fruit upon silver trees;
One by one the casements catch
Her beams beneath the silvery thatch;
Couched in his kennel, like a log,
With paws of silver sleeps the dog;
From their shadowy cote the white breasts peep
Of doves in a silver-feathered sleep;
A harvest mouse goes scampering by,
With silver claws, and silver eye;
And moveless fish in the water gleam,
By silver reeds in a silver stream.

                  WALTER DE LA MARE

TO THE EVENING STAR

Thou fair-haired Angel of the Evening,
Now, whilst the sun rests on the mountains, light
Thy bright torch of love: thy radiant crown
Put on, and smile upon our evening bed.

Smile on our loves, and, while thou drawest the
Blue curtains of the sky, scatter thy silver dew
On every flower that shuts its sweet eyes
In timely sleep. Let thy west wind sleep on
The lake; speak silence with thy glimmering eyes,
And wash the dusk with silver.—Soon, full soon,
Dost thou withdraw; then the wolf rages wide,
And the lion glares through the dun forest:
The fleeces of our flocks are covered with
Thy sacred dew: protect them with thine influence!

WILLIAM BLAKE

SISTER, AWAKE!

Sister, awake! close not your eyes,
   The day her light discloses;
And the bright morning doth arise
   Out of her bed of roses.
See the clear sun, the world's bright eye,
   In at our window peeping;
Lo, how he blusheth to espy
   Us idle wenches sleeping!
Therefore wake, make haste I say,
   And let us without staying
All in our gowns of green so gay
   Into the park a-maying.

ANONYMOUS

AUTUMN TO SUMMER

AUTUMN

I love the fitful gust that shakes
 The casement all the day,
And from the glossy elm-tree takes
 The faded leaves away,
Twirling them by the window pane
With thousand others down the lane.

I love to see the shaking twig
 Dance till the shut of eve,
The sparrow on the cottage rig,
 Whose chirp would make believe
That Spring was just now flirting by
In Summer's lap with flowers to lie.

I love to see the cottage smoke
 Curl upwards through the trees,
The pigeons nestled round the cote
 On November days like these:
The cock upon the dunghill crowing,
The mill-sails on the heath a-going.

The feather from the raven's breast
    Falls on the stubble lea,
The acorns near the old crow's nest
    Drop pattering down the tree:
The grunting pigs that wait for all,
Scramble and hurry where they fall.

JOHN CLARE

TO AUTUMN

Season of mists and mellow fruitfulness!
    Close bosom-friend of the maturing sun;
Conspiring with him how to load and bless
    With fruit the vines that round the thatch-eaves run;
To bend with apples the moss'd cottage-trees,
    And fill all fruit with ripeness to the core;
      To swell the gourd, and plump the hazel shells
    With a sweet kernel; to set budding more,
And still more, later flowers for the bees,
Until they think warm days will never cease,
      For Summer has o'er-brimm'd their clammy cells.

Who hath not seen thee oft amid thy store?
    Sometimes whoever seeks abroad may find
Thee sitting careless on a granary floor,
    Thy hair soft-lifted by the winnowing wind;
Or on a half-reap'd furrow sound asleep,
    Drowsed with the fumes of poppies, while thy hook
      Spares the next swath and all its twinèd flowers;

And sometimes like a gleaner thou dost keep
　　Steady thy laden head across a brook;
　　Or by a cider-press, with patient look,
　　　Thou watchest the last oozings, hours by hours.

Where are the songs of Spring?　Ay, where are they?
　　Think not of them, thou hast thy music too,
While barrèd clouds bloom the soft-dying day,
　　And touch the stubble-plains with rosy hue;
Then in a wailful choir the small gnats mourn
　　Among the river sallows, borne aloft
　　　Or sinking as the light wind lives or dies;
And full-grown lambs loud bleat from hilly bourn;
　　Hedge-crickets sing; and now with treble soft
　　The redbreast whistles from a garden-croft,
　　　And gathering swallows twitter in the skies.

JOHN KEATS

BLOW, BLOW, THOU WINTER WIND

　　　Blow, blow, thou winter wind,
　　　Thou art not so unkind
　　　　As man's ingratitude;
　　　Thy tooth is not so keen,
　　　Because thou art not seen,
　　　　Although thy breath be rude.
Heigh-ho! sing, heigh-ho! unto the green holly:
Most friendship is feigning, most loving mere folly:
　　　Then heigh-ho, the holly!
　　　　This life is most jolly.

Freeze, freeze, thou bitter sky,
That dost not bite so nigh
　　As benefits forgot:
Though thou the waters warp,[1]
Thy sting is not so sharp
　　As friend remember'd not.
Heigh-ho! sing, heigh-ho! unto the green holly:
Most friendship is feigning, most loving mere folly:
　　Then heigh-ho, the holly!
　　This life is most jolly.

WILLIAM SHAKESPEARE

[1] To shrivel or wrinkle through shrinkage in cold weather.

THE SONG OF THE STARING OWL

When icicles hang by the wall,
　　And Dick the shepherd blows his nail,
And Tom bears logs into the hall,
　　And milk comes frozen home in pail,
When blood is nipped, and ways be foul,
Then nightly sings the staring owl,
　　　　　　　　　　Tu-who;
　　Tu-whit, tu-who—a merry note,
While greasy Joan doth keel[1] the pot.

When all aloud the wind doth blow,
　　And coughing drowns the parson's saw,[2]

[1] To cool by stirring or skimming.　　[2] Wise saying.

And birds sit brooding in the snow,
　And Marian's nose looks red and raw,
When roasted crabs[1] hiss in the bowl,
Then nightly sings the staring owl,
　　　　　　　　　Tu-who;
　Tu-whit, tu-who—a merry note,
While greasy Joan doth keel the pot.

WILLIAM SHAKESPEARE

A WINTER SONG

Up in the morning's no for me,
Up in the morning early;
When a' the hills are cover'd wi' snaw
I'm sure it's winter fairly.

Cauld blaws the wind frae east to west,
The drift is driving sairly;
Sae loud and shrill's I hear the blast,
I'm sure it's winter fairly.
　Up in the morning, etc.

The birds sit chittering in the thorn,
A' day they fare but sparely;
And lang's the night frae e'en to morn;
I'm sure it's winter fairly.
　Up in the morning, etc.

ROBERT BURNS

[1] Crab apples.

297

SKATING

And in the frosty season, when the sun
Was set, and visible for many a mile
The cottage windows blazed through twilight
    gloom,
I heeded not their summons: happy time
It was indeed for all of us—for me
It was a time of rapture!   Clear and loud
The village clock tolled six,—I wheeled about,
Proud and exulting like an untired horse
That cares not for his home. All shod with steel,
We hissed along the polished ice in games
Confederate, imitative of the chase
And woodland pleasures,—the resounding horn,
The pack loud chiming, and the hunted hare.
So through the darkness and the cold we flew,
And not a voice was idle; with the din
Smitten, the precipices rang aloud;
The leafless trees and every icy crag
Tinkled like iron; while far distant hills
Into the tumult sent an alien sound
Of melancholy not unnoticed, while the stars
Eastward were sparkling clear, and in the west
The orange sky of evening died away.
Not seldom from the uproar I retired
Into a silent bay, or sportively
Glanced sideway, leaving the tumultuous throng,
To cut across the reflex of a star
That fled, and, flying still before me, gleamed

Upon the glassy plain; and oftentimes,
When we had given our bodies to the wind,
And all the shadowy banks on either side
Came sweeping through the darkness, spinning
    still
The rapid line of motion, then at once
Have I, reclining back upon my heels,
Stopped short; yet still the solitary cliffs
Wheeled by me—even as if the earth had rolled
With visible motion her diurnal round!
Behind me did they stretch in solemn train,
Feebler and feebler, and I stood and watched
Till all was tranquil as a dreamless sleep.

                    WILLIAM WORDSWORTH

OLD WINTER

Old Winter, sad, in snow yclad,
   Is making a doleful din;
But let him howl till he crack his jowl,
   We will not let him in.

Ay, let him lift from the billowy drift
   His hoary, haggard form,
And scowling stand, with his wrinkled hand
   Outstretching to the storm.

And let his weird and sleety beard
   Stream loose upon the blast,

And, rustling, chime to the tinkling rime
  From his bald head falling fast.

Let his baleful breath shed blight and death
  On herb and flower and tree;
And brooks and ponds in crystal bonds
  Bind fast, but what care we?

Let him push at the door, in the chimney roar,
  And rattle the window pane;
Let him in at us spy with his icicle eye,
  But he shall not entrance gain.

Let him gnaw, forsooth, with his freezing tooth,
  On our roof-tiles, till he tire;
But we care not a whit, as we jovial sit
  Before our blazing fire.

Come, lads, let's sing, till the rafters ring;
  Come push the can about—
From our snug fireside this Christmas-tide
  We'll keep old Winter out.

                                        T. NOEL

LONDON SNOW

When men were all asleep the snow came flying,
  In large white flakes falling on the city brown,
Stealthily and perpetually settling and loosely lying,
  Hushing the latest traffic of the drowsy town;

Deadening, muffling, stifling its murmurs failing;
Lazily and incessantly floating down and down:
  Silently sifting and veiling road, roof and railing;
Hiding difference, making unevenness even,
Into angles and crevices softly drifting and sailing.
  All night it fell, and when full inches seven
It lay in the depth of its uncompacted lightness,
The clouds blew off from a high and frosty heaven;
  And all woke earlier for the unaccustomed brightness
Of the winter dawning, the strange unheavenly glare:
The eye marvelled—marvelled at the dazzling white-
     ness;
  The ear hearkened to the stillness of the solemn air;
No sound of wheel rumbling nor of foot falling,
And the busy morning cries came thin and spare.
  Then boys I heard, as they went to school, calling,
They gathered up the crystal manna to freeze
Their tongues with tasting, their hands with snow-
     balling;
  Or rioted in a drift, plunging up to the knees;
Or peering up from under the white-mossed wonder,
"O look at the trees!" they cried, "O look at the
     trees!"
  With lessened load a few carts creak and blunder,
Following along the white deserted way,
A country company long dispersed asunder:
  When now already the sun, in pale display
Standing by Paul's high dome, spread forth below
His sparkling beams, and awoke the stir of the day.
  For now doors open, and war is waged with the snow;
And trains of sombre men, past tale of number,
Tread long brown paths, as toward their toil they go;

But even for them awhile no cares encumber
Their minds diverted; the daily word is unspoken,
The daily thoughts of labour and sorrow slumber
At the sight of the beauty that greets them, for the
    charm they have broken.

ROBERT BRIDGES

SNOW IN THE SUBURBS

Every branch big with it,
  Bent every twig with it;
Every fork like a white web-foot;
Every street and pavement mute:
Some flakes have lost their way, and grope back
    upward, when
Meeting those meandering down they turn and
    descend again.
The palings are glued together like a wall,
And there is no waft of wind with the fleecy
    fall.

A sparrow enters the tree,
  Whereon immediately
A snow-lump thrice his own slight size
Descends on him and showers his head and
    eyes,
  And overturns him,
  And near inurns him,

And lights on a nether twig, when its brush
Starts off a volley of other lodging lumps with
    a rush.

    The steps are a blanched slope,
    Up which, with feeble hope,
A black cat comes, wide-eyed and thin;
    And we take him in.

THOMAS HARDY

SPRING, THE SWEET SPRING

Spring, the sweet Spring, is the year's pleasant king;
Then blooms each thing, then maids dance in a ring,
Cold doth not sting, the pretty birds do sing,
    Cuckoo, jug-jug, pu-we, to-witta-woo!

The palm and may make country houses gay,
Lambs frisk and play, the shepherds pipe all day,
And we hear aye birds tune this merry lay,
    Cuckoo, jug-jug, pu-we, to-witta-woo!

The fields breathe sweet, the daisies kiss our feet,
Young lovers meet, old wives a-sunning sit,
In every street these tunes our ears do greet,
    Cuckoo, jug-jug, pu-we, to-witta-woo!
      Spring! the sweet Spring!

THOMAS NASH

CUCKOO SONG

Sumer is icumen in,
    Lhude sing cuccu!
Groweth sed, and bloweth med,
    And springeth the wude nu—
           Sing cuccu!

Awe[1] bleteth after lomb,
    Lhouth[2] after calve cu;
Bulluc sterteth,[3] bucke verteth,[4]
    Murie sing cuccu!

Cuccu, cuccu, well singès thu, cuccu:
    Ne swike[5] thu naver nu;
Sing cuccu, nu, sing cuccu,
    Sing cuccu, sing cuccu, nu!
               ANONYMOUS (about 1250)

[1] Ewe.   [2] Loweth.   [3] Jumps about.
    [4] Turns and twists about.   [5] Cease.

THE PILGRIM: HIS CHARACTER

THE VALOROUS PILGRIM

Who would true valour see,
    Let him come hither;
One here will constant be,
    Come wind, come weather;
There's no discouragement
Shall make him once relent
His first avowed intent
        To be a pilgrim.

Whoso beset him round
    With dismal stories,
Do but themselves confound,
    His strength the more is.
No lion can him fright;
He'll with a giant fight,
But he will have a right
        To be a pilgrim.

Hobgoblin nor foul fiend
    Can daunt his spirit;
He knows he at the end
    Shall life inherit.

Then fancies fly away,
He'll not fear what men say,
He'll labour night and day
    To be a pilgrim.

JOHN BUNYAN

A MAN'S A MAN FOR A' THAT

Is there for honest poverty
    That hangs his head, and a' that?
The coward-slave, we pass him by,
    We dare be poor for a' that!
For a' that, and a' that,
    Our toils obscure, and a' that;
The rank is but the guinea's stamp,
    The man's the gowd for a' that.

What though on hamely fare we dine,
    Wear hoddin[1] grey, and a' that;
Gie fools their silks, and knaves their wine,
    A man's a man for a' that.
For a' that, and a' that,
    Their tinsel show, and a' that,
The honest man, though e'er sae poor,
    Is king o' men for a' that.

You see yon birkie, ca'd a lord,
    Wha struts, and stares, and a' that;
Though hundreds worship at his word,
    He's but a coof[2] for a' that:

[1] Coarse woollen cloth.   [2] Stupid fellow.

306

For a' that, and a' that,
  His riband, star and a' that.
The man of independent mind,
  He looks and laughs at a' that!

A king can mak' a belted knight,
  A marquis, duke, and a' that;
But an honest man's aboon his might,
  Guid faith he mauna fa' that!
For a' that, and a' that,
  Their dignities, and a' that,
The pith o' sense, and pride o' worth
  Are higher rank than a' that.

Then let us pray that come it may—
  As come it will, for a' that—
That sense and worth, o'er a' the earth,
  May bear the gree,[1] and a' that;
For a' that, and a' that,
  It's comin' yet for a' that,
That man to man, the warld o'er,
  Shall brothers be for a' that.

ROBERT BURNS

THE SECRET OF CONTENTMENT

He that is down, needs fear no fall,
  He that is low, no pride;
He that is humble ever shall
  Have God to be his guide.

[1] Carry off the prize for victory.

I am content with what I have,
    Little be it, or much;
And, Lord, contentment still I crave,
    Because Thou savest such.

Fullness to such a burden is
    That go on pilgrimage :
Here little, and hereafter bliss,
    Is best from age to age.

JOHN BUNYAN

ON HIS BLINDNESS

When I consider how my light is spent
Ere half my days, in this dark world and wide,
And that one talent which is death to hide,
Lodged with me useless, though my soul more bent
To serve therewith my Maker, and present
My true account, lest He, returning, chide,—
" Doth God exact day-labour, light denied? "
I fondly ask.   But Patience, to prevent
That murmur, soon replies, " God doth not need
Either man's work, or His own gifts : who best
Bear His mild yoke, they serve Him best : His state
Is kingly : thousands at His bidding speed
And post o'er land and ocean without rest :
They also serve who only stand and wait."

JOHN MILTON

THE PILGRIM: HIS LOVE OF COUNTRY

THE SOUTH COUNTRY

When I am living in the Midlands,
   That are sodden and unkind,
I light my lamp in the evening:
   My work is left behind;
And the great hills of the South Country
   Come back into my mind.

The great hills of the South Country
   They stand along the sea,
And it's there, walking in the high woods,
   That I could wish to be,
And the men that were boys when I was a boy
   Walking along with me.

The men that live in North England
   I saw them for a day:
Their hearts are set upon the waste fells,
   Their skies are fast and grey;
From their castle-walls a man may see
   The mountains far away

The men that live in West England
  They see the Severn strong,
A-rolling on rough water brown
  Light aspen leaves along.
They have the secret of the Rocks
  And the oldest kind of song.

But the men that live in the South Country
  Are the kindest and most wise,
They get their laughter from the loud surf,
  And the faith in their happy eyes
Comes surely from our Sister the Spring
  When over the sea she flies;
The violets suddenly bloom at her feet,
  She blesses us with surprise.

I never get between the pines
  But I smell the Sussex air;
Nor I never come on a belt of sand
  But my home is there.
And along the sky the line of the Downs
  So noble and so bare.

A lost thing could I never find,
  Nor a broken thing mend:
And I fear I shall be all alone
  When I get towards the end.
Who will there be to comfort me
  Or who will be my friend?

I will gather and carefully make my friends
  Of the men of the Sussex Weald;

They watch the stars from silent folds,
    They stiffly plough the field.
By them and the God of the South Country
    My poor soul shall be healed.

If I ever become a rich man,
    Or if ever I grow to be old,
I will build a house with deep thatch
    To shelter me from the cold,
And there shall the Sussex songs be sung
    And the story of Sussex told.

I will hold my house in the high wood,
    Within a walk of the sea,
And the men that were boys when I was a boy
    Shall sit and drink with me.

                                    HILAIRE BELLOC

THE NEW JERUSALEM

And did those feet in ancient time
    Walk upon England's mountains green?
And was the holy Lamb of God
    On England's pleasant pastures seen?

And did the Countenance Divine
    Shine forth upon our clouded hills?
And was Jerusalem builded here
    Among these dark Satanic mills?

Bring me my bow of burning gold!
  Bring me my arrows of desire!
Bring me my spear! O clouds, unfold!
  Bring me my chariot of fire!

I will not cease from mental fight,
  Nor shall my sword sleep in my hand,
Till we have built Jerusalem
  In England's green and pleasant land.

WILLIAM BLAKE

FAREWELL

JUGGLING JERRY

I

Pitch here the tent, while the old horse
   grazes:
  By the old hedge-side we'll halt a stage.
It's nigh my last above the daisies:
  My next leaf'll be man's blank page.
Yes, my old girl! and it's no use crying:
  Juggler, constable, king, must bow.
One that outjuggles all's been spying
  Long to have me, and he has me now.

II

We've travelled times to this old common:
  Often we've hung our pots in the gorse.
We've had a stirring life, old woman,
  You, and I, and the old grey horse.
Races, and fairs, and royal occasions,
  Found us coming to their call:
Now they'll miss us at our stations:
  There's a Juggler outjuggles all!

III

Up goes the lark, as if all were jolly!
    Over the duck-pond the willow shakes.
Easy to think that grieving's folly,
    When the hand's firm as driven stakes!
Ay, when we're strong, and braced, and manful,
    Life's a sweet fiddle: but we're a batch
Born to become the Great Juggler's han'ful:
    Balls he shies up, and is safe to catch.

IV

Here's where the lads of the village cricket:
    I was a lad not wide from here:
Couldn't I whip off the bail from the wicket?
    Like an old world those days appear!
Donkey, sheep, geese, and thatched ale-house—
    I know them!
    They are old friends of my halts, and seem,
Somehow, as if kind thanks I owe them:
    Juggling don't hinder the heart's esteem.

V

Juggling's no sin, for we must have victual:
    Nature allows us to bait for the fool.
Holding one's own makes us juggle no little;
    But, to increase it, hard juggling's the rule.
You that are sneering at my profession,
    Haven't you juggled a vast amount?
There's the Prime Minister, in one Session,
    Juggles more games than my sins'll count.

VI

I've murdered insects with mock thunder:
　　Conscience, for that, in men don't quail.
I've made bread from the bump of wonder:
　　That's my business, and there's my tale.
Fashion and rank all praised the professor:
　　Ay! and I've had my smile from the Queen:
Bravo, Jerry! she meant: God bless her!
　　Ain't this a sermon on that scene?

VII

I've studied men from my topsy-turvy
　　Close, and, I reckon, rather true.
Some are fine fellows: some, right scurvy:
　　Most, a dash between the two.
But it's a woman, old girl, that makes me
　　Think more kindly of the race:
And it's a woman, old girl, that shakes me
　　When the Great Juggler I must face.

VIII

We two were married, due and legal:
　　Honest we've lived since we've been one.
Lord! I could then jump like an eagle:
　　You danced bright as a bit o' the sun.
Birds in a May-bush we were! right merry!
　　All night we kiss'd, we juggled all day.
Joy was the heart of Juggling Jerry!
　　Now from his old girl he's juggled away.

IX

It's past parsons to console us:
   No, nor no doctor fetch for me:
I can die without my bolus[1]:
   Two of a trade, lass, never agree!
Parson and Doctor!—don't they love rarely
   Fighting the devil in other men's fields!
Stand up yourself and match him fairly:
   Then see how the rascal yields!

X

I, lass, have lived no gipsy, flaunting
   Finery while his poor helpmate grubs:
Coin I've stored, and you won't be wanting:
   You shan't beg from the troughs and tubs.
Nobly you've stuck to me, though in his kitchen
   Many a Marquis would hail you Cook!
Palaces you could have ruled and grown rich in,
   But your old Jerry you never forsook.

XI

Hand up the chirper! ripe ale winks in it;
   Let's have comfort and be at peace.
Once a stout draught made me light as a linnet.
   Cheer up! the Lord must have his lease.
Maybe—for none see in that black hollow—
   It's just a place where we're held in pawn,
And, when the Great Juggler makes as to swallow
   It's just the sword-trick—I ain't quite gone!

[1] A contemptuous word for a pill.

XII

Yonder came smells of the gorse, so nutty,
    Gold-like and warm: it's the prime of May.
Better than mortar, brick and putty
    Is God's house on a blowing day.
Lean me more up the mound; now I feel it:
    All the old heath-smells! Ain't it strange?
There's the world laughing, as if to conceal it,
    But He's by us, juggling the change.

XIII

I mind it well, by the sea-beach lying,
    Once—it's long gone—when two gulls we
      beheld,
Which, as the moon got up, were flying
    Down a big wave that sparked and swelled.
Crack, went a gun: one fell: the second
    Wheeled round him twice, and was off for
      new luck:
There in the dark her white wing beckon'd:—
    Drop me a kiss—I'm the bird dead-struck!

GEORGE MEREDITH

ALL THAT'S PAST

Very old are the woods;
    And the buds that break
Out of the briar's boughs,
    When March winds wake,

So old with their beauty are—
    Oh, no man knows
Through what wild centuries
    Roves back the rose.

Very old are the brooks;
    And the rills that rise
Where snow sleeps cold beneath
    The azure skies
Sing such a history
    Of come and gone,
Their every drop is as wise
    As Solomon.

Very old are we men;
    Our dreams are tales
Told in dim Eden
    By Eve's nightingales;
We wake and whisper awhile,
    But, the day gone by,
Silence and sleep like fields
    Of amaranth[1] lie.

WALTER DE LA MARE

ODE WRITTEN IN 1746

How sleep the brave, who sink to rest
By all their country's wishes blest!
When Spring, with dewy fingers cold,

[1] An imaginary, fadeless flower.

Returns to deck their hallow'd mould,
She there shall dress a sweeter sod
Than Fancy's feet have ever trod.

By fairy hands their knell is rung;
By forms unseen their dirge is sung;
There Honour comes, a pilgrim grey,
To bless the turf that wraps their clay;
And Freedom shall awhile repair
To dwell a weeping hermit there!

WILLIAM COLLINS

CORONACH[1]

He is gone on the mountain,
  He is lost to the forest,
Like a summer-dried fountain,
  When our need was the sorest,
The font, reappearing,
  From the rain-drops shall borrow,
But to us comes no cheering,
  To Duncan no morrow!

The hand of the reaper
  Takes the ears that are hoary,
But the voice of the weeper
  Wails manhood in glory.
The autumn winds rushing
  Waft the leaves that are serest,
But our flower was in flushing,
  When blighting was nearest.

[1] A funeral song in the Highlands.

Fleet foot on the correi,[1]
   Sage counsel in cumber,[2]
Red hand in the foray,
   How sound is thy slumber!
Like the dew on the mountain,
   Like the foam on the river,
Like the bubble on the fountain,
   Thou art gone, and for ever!

SIR WALTER SCOTT

OZYMANDIAS

I met a traveller from an antique land
Who said: Two vast and trunkless legs of stone
Stand in the desert. Near them, on the sand,
Half sunk, a shatter'd visage lies, whose frown,
And wrinkled lip, and sneer of cold command,
Tell that its sculptor well those passions read
Which yet survive, stamp'd on these lifeless things,
The hand that mock'd them and the heart that fed;
And on the pedestal these words appear:
" My name is Ozymandias, king of kings:
Look on my works, ye Mighty, and despair! "
Nothing beside remains. Round the decay
Of that colossal wreck, boundless and bare
The lone and level sands stretch far away.

PERCY BYSSHE SHELLEY

[1] Mountain hollow where stags gather.   [2] Trouble or distress.

THE LADY OF SHALOTT

Part I

On either side the river lie
Long fields of barley and of rye,
That clothe the wold and meet the sky;
And thro' the field the road runs by
 To many-tower'd Camelot;
And up and down the people go,
Gazing where the lilies blow,
Round an island there below,
 The island of Shalott.

Willows whiten, aspens quiver,
Little breezes dusk and shiver
Thro' the wave that runs for ever
By the island in the river
 Flowing down to Camelot.
Four grey walls, and four grey towers,
Overlook a space of flowers,
And the silent isle imbowers
 The Lady of Shalott.

By the margin, willow-veil'd,
Slide the heavy barges trail'd
By slow horses; and unhail'd
The shallop flitteth silken-sail'd
 Skimming down to Camelot:
But who hath seen her wave her hand?
Or at the casement seen her stand?
Or is she known in all the land,
 The Lady of Shalott?

Only reapers, reaping early
In among the bearded barley,
Hear a song that echoes cheerly
From the river winding clearly,
    Down to tower'd Camelot:
And by the moon the reaper weary,
Piling sheaves in uplands airy,
Listening, whispers, " 'Tis the fairy
    Lady of Shalott."

Part II

There she weaves by night and day
A magic web with colours gay,
She has heard a whisper say,
A curse is on her if she stay
    To look down to Camelot.
She knows not what the curse may be,
And so she weaveth steadily,
And little other care hath she,
    The Lady of Shalott.

And moving thro' a mirror clear
That hangs before her all the year,
Shadows of the world appear.
There she sees the highway near
    Winding down to Camelot:
There the river eddy whirls,
And there the surly village-churls,
And the red cloaks of market girls,
    Pass onward from Shalott.

Sometimes a troop of damsels glad,
An abbot on an ambling pad,
Sometimes a curly shepherd-lad,
Or long-hair'd page in crimson clad,
    Goes by to tower'd Camelot;
And sometimes thro' the mirror blue
The knights come riding two and two:
She hath no loyal knight and true,
    The Lady of Shalott.

But in her web she still delights
To weave the mirror's magic sights,
For often thro' the silent nights
A funeral, with plumes and lights
    And music, went to Camelot:
Or when the moon was overhead,
Came two young lovers lately wed;
"I am half sick of shadows," said
    The Lady of Shalott.

Part III

A bow-shot from her bower-eaves,
He rode between the barley-sheaves,
The sun came dazzling thro' the leaves,
And flamed upon the brazen greaves
    Of bold Sir Lancelot.
A red-cross knight for ever kneel'd
To a lady in his shield,
That sparkled on the yellow field,
    Beside remote Shalott.

The gemmy bridle glitter'd free,
Like to some branch of stars we see
Hung in the golden Galaxy.
The bridle bells rang merrily
    As he rode down to Camelot:
And from his blazon'd baldric slung
A mighty silver bugle hung,
And as he rode his armour rung,
      Beside remote Shalott.

All in the blue unclouded weather
Thick-jewell'd shone the saddle leather,
The helmet and the helmet-feather
Burn'd like one burning flame together,
    As he rode down to Camelot.
As often thro' the purple night,
Below the starry clusters bright,
Some bearded meteor, trailing light,
    Moves over still Shalott.

His broad clear brow in sunlight glow'd;
On burnish'd hooves his war-horse trode;
From underneath his helmet flow'd
His coal-black curls as on he rode,
    As he rode down to Camelot.
From the bank and from the river
He flash'd into the crystal mirror,
" Tirra lirra," by the river
    Sang Sir Lancelot.

She left the web, she left the loom,
She made three paces thro' the room,

She saw the water-lily bloom,
She saw the helmet and the plume,
    She look'd down to Camelot.
Out flew the web and floated wide;
The mirror crack'd from side to side;
" The curse is come upon me," cried
    The Lady of Shalott.

PART IV

In the stormy east-wind straining,
The pale yellow woods were waning,
The broad stream in his banks complaining,
Heavily the low sky raining
    Over tower'd Camelot;
Down she came and found a boat
Beneath a willow left afloat,
And round about the prow she wrote
    The Lady of Shalott.

And down the river's dim expanse
Like some bold seër in a trance,
Seeking all his own mischance—
With a glassy countenance
    Did she look to Camelot.
And at the closing of the day
She loosed the chain, and down she lay;
The broad stream bore her far away,
    The Lady of Shalott.

Lying, robed in snowy white
That loosely flew to left and right—

The leaves upon her falling light—
Thro' the noises of the night
    She floated down to Camelot:
And as the boat-head wound along
The willowy hills and fields among,
They heard her singing her last song,
    The Lady of Shalott.

Heard a carol, mournful, holy,
Chanted loudly, chanted lowly,
Till her blood was frozen slowly,
And her eyes were darken'd wholly,
    Turn'd to tower'd Camelot;
For ere she reach'd upon the tide
The first house by the water-side,
Singing in her song she died,
    The Lady of Shalott.

Under tower and balcony,
By garden-wall and gallery,
A gleaming shape she floated by,
Dead-pale between the houses high,
    Silent into Camelot.
Out upon the wharfs they came,
Knight and burgher, lord and dame,
And round the prow they read her name,
    The Lady of Shalott.

Who is this? and what is here?
And in the lighted palace near
Died the sound of royal cheer;
And they cross'd themselves for fear,

All the knights at Camelot:
But Lancelot mused a little space;
He said, " She has a lovely face;
God in His mercy lend her grace,
    The Lady of Shalott."

LORD TENNYSON

THE BURIAL SONG FROM " CYMBELINE "

Fear no more the heat o' the sun,
   Nor the furious winter's rages;
Thou thy worldly task hast done,
   Home art gone, and ta'en thy wages;
Golden lads and girls all must,
As chimney-sweepers, come to dust.

Fear no more the frown o' the great,
   Thou art past the tyrant's stroke:
Care no more to clothe and eat;
   To thee the reed is as the oak:
The sceptre, learning, physic, must
All follow this, and come to dust.

Fear no more the lightning-flash,
   Nor the all-dreaded thunder-stone;
Fear not slander, censure rash;
   Thou hast finished joy and moan:
All lovers young, all lovers must
Consign to thee, and come to dust.

No exorciser harm thee!
Nor no witchcraft charm thee!
Ghost unlaid forbear thee!
Nothing ill come near thee!
Quiet consummation have;
And renownèd be thy grave!

WILLIAM SHAKESPEARE

SILENCE

There is a silence where hath been no sound,
　There is a silence where no sound may be,
　In the cold grave—under the deep, deep sea,
Or in wide desert where no life is found,
Which hath been mute, and still must sleep profound;
　No voice is hushed—no life treads silently,
　But clouds and cloudy shadows wander free,
That never spoke, over the idle ground:
But in green ruins, in the desolate walls
　Of antique palaces where Man hath been,
Though the dun fox or wild hyena calls,
　And owls, that flit continually between,
Shriek to the echo, and the low winds moan—
There the true Silence is, self-conscious and alone.

THOMAS HOOD

INDEX OF AUTHORS

INDEX OF AUTHORS

INDEX OF FIRST LINES